JUMP Math 2.2

Book 2 Part 2 of 2

Contents

jump math™

MULTIPLYING POTENTIAL.

JUMP Math
One Yonge Street, Suite 1014
Toronto, Ontario M5E 1E5
Canada
www.jumpmath.org

Writers: Dr. Francisco Kibedi, Dr. Anna Klebanov
Editors: Megan Burns, Liane Tsui, Natalie Francis, Lindsay Karpenko, Daniel Polowin, Jackie Dulson,
         Janice Dyer, Dawn Hunter, Michelle MacAleese, Louise MacKenzie, Leanne Rancourt
Layout and Illustrations: Linh Lam, Fely Guinasao-Fernandes, Sawyer Paul
Cover Design: Blakeley Words+Pictures
Cover Photograph: © adriennexplores/Shutterstock

ISBN 978-1-928134-34-3

Third printing June 2019

Printed and bound in Canada

Welcome to JUMP Math

Entering the world of JUMP Math means believing that every child has the capacity to be fully numerate and to love math. Founder and mathematician John Mighton has used this premise to develop his innovative teaching method. The resulting resources isolate and describe concepts so clearly and incrementally that everyone can understand them.

JUMP Math is comprised of teacher's guides (which are the heart of our program), interactive whiteboard lessons, student assessment & practice books, evaluation materials, outreach programs, and teacher training. All of this is presented on the JUMP Math website: **www.jumpmath.org**.

Teacher's guides are available on the website for free use. Read the introduction to the teacher's guides before you begin using these resources. This will ensure that you understand both the philosophy and the methodology of JUMP Math. The assessment & practice books are designed for use by students, with adult guidance. Each student will have unique needs and it is important to provide the student with the appropriate support and encouragement as he or she works through the material.

Allow students to discover the concepts by themselves as much as possible. Mathematical discoveries can be made in small, incremental steps. The discovery of a new step is like untangling the parts of a puzzle. It is exciting and rewarding.

Students will need to answer the questions marked with a ▱ in a notebook. Grid paper notebooks should always be on hand for answering extra questions or when additional room for calculation is needed.

Contents

Unit 5: Geometry: 2-D Shapes

Unit 6: Probability and Data Management: Sorting and Graphing

Unit 7: Number Sense: Addition and Subtraction with Numbers to 100

Unit 8: Geometry: Symmetry

Unit 9: Number Sense: Equations and Word Problems

Unit 10: Number Sense: Using 10 to Add and Subtract

Unit 11: Measurement: More Length and Mass

PART 2

Unit 12: Number Sense: Skip Counting and Estimating

Unit 13: Number Sense: Addition Strategies

Unit 14: Number Sense: Subtraction Strategies

Unit 15: Patterns and Algebra: Growing and Shrinking Patterns

Unit 16: Geometry: 3-D Shapes

Unit 17: Number Sense: Money

Unit 18: Number Sense: Fractions, Multiplication, and Division

Unit 19: Measurement: Time

Unit 20: Probability and Data Management: Probability

Unit 21: Measurement: Area, Calendars, Temperature, and Capacity

Skip Counting by 2s

Count by 2s and colour the numbers that you say.

☐ Start at **2** and colour the numbers **blue**.
☐ Start at **1** and colour the numbers **red**.

1	2	3	4	5	6	7	8	9	10
11	12	13	14	15	16	17	18	19	20
21	22	23	24	25	26	27	28	29	30
31	32	33	34	35	36	37	38	39	40

The blue numbers have ones digit _2_, _4_, _6_, _8_, or _10_.

The red numbers have ones digit ___, ___, ___, ___, or ___.

☐ Count by 2s.

2 ____ ____ ____ ____ ____ _14_

42 ____ ____ ____ ____ ____ ____

86 ____ ____ ____ _94_ ____ ____

1 ____ ____ ____ _9_ ____ ____

61 ____ ____ ____ ____ ____ ____

☐ Count back by 2s.

86 _84_ ____ ____ ____ _76_ ____

1

Skip Counting by 5s and 10s

☐ Start at **5** and count by 5s. Colour the numbers that you say.

1	2	3	4	5	6	7	8	9	10
11	12	13	14	15	16	17	18	19	20
21	22	23	24	25	26	27	28	29	30

The coloured numbers have ones digit _____ or _____.

☐ Count by 5s.

0 _5_ _10_ _15_ _2530_ _3540_

60 _65_ ____ ____ ____ ____ ____

70 ____ ____ ____ ____ _95_ ____

☐ Count back by 5s.

30 _25_ ____ ____ ____ ____ ____

80 ____ ____ ____ ____ _55_ ____

100 ____ ____ _85_ ____ ____ ____

☐ Count by 2s and then by 1s to see how many.

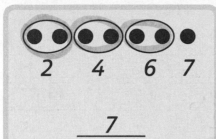

2 4 6 7

_7_

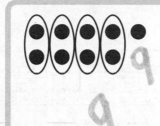

9

_9_

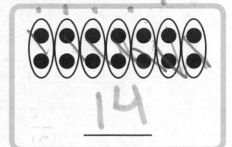

_14_

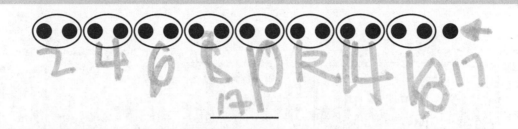

2 4 6 8 10 12 14 16 17

_____

☐ Count by 5s and then by 1s to see how many.

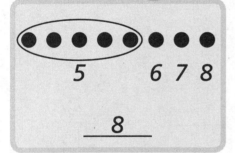

5 6 7 8

_8_

5 10 15

_16_

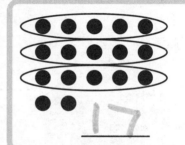

_17_

     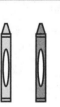

_____

A B C D E F G H I J K L M N O
P Q R S T U V W X Y Z

There are _26_ letters in the alphabet.

☐ Count how many.
   Use groups of 10.

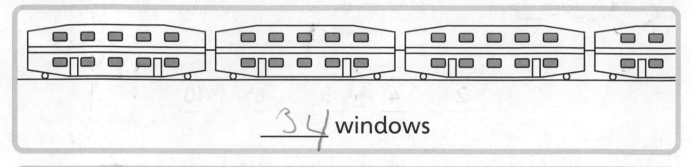

____34____ windows

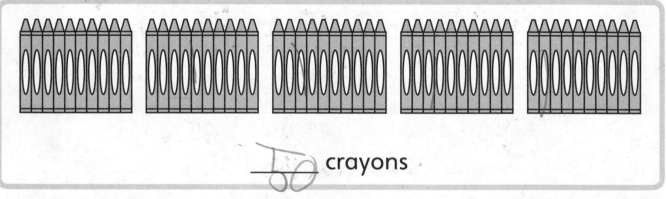

____50____ crayons

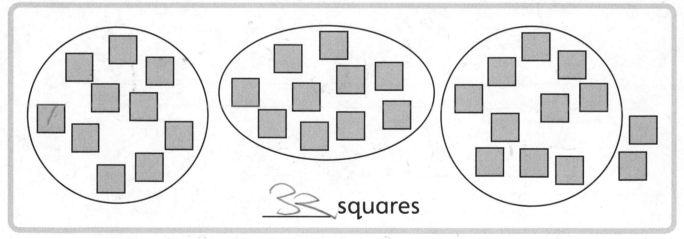

____32____ squares

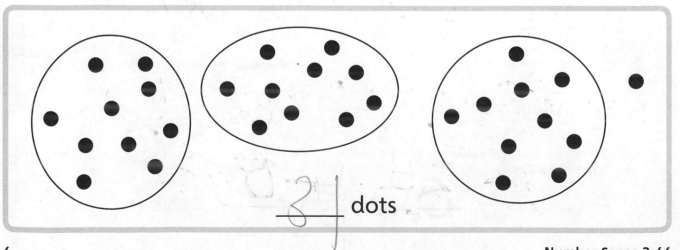

____31____ dots

4

Count by 10s and colour the numbers that you say.

☐ Start at **10** and colour the numbers **red**.
☐ Start at **7** and colour the numbers **blue**.

1	2	3	4	5	6	7	8	9	10
11	12	13	14	15	16	17	18	19	20
21	22	23	24	25	26	27	28	29	30
31	32	33	34	35	36	37	38	39	40

The red numbers have ones digit _____.

The blue numbers have ones digit _____.

☐ Count by 10s.

20 _30_ _40_ 50 _60_ _70_ _80_

40 _50_ _60_ _70_ _80_ 90 _100_

37 _47_ _57_ _67_ 77 _87_ _07_

22 _32_ _42_ _52_ _62_ _72_ _82_

15 _25_ _35_ _45_ _55_ _65_ _7_

If you can count back from 10 by 1s

| 10 | 9 | 8 | 7 | ... |

Then you can count back from 100 by 10s

| 100 | 90 | 80 | 70 | ... |

And from 93 by 10s

| 93 | 83 | 73 | 63 | ... |

☐ Count back by 10s.

100   _90_   _80_   _70_   _60_   _50_

53   _43_   _33_   _23_   _13_   _3_

80   _70_   _60_   _50_   _40_   _30_

76   _66_   _56_   _46_   _36_   _26_

65   _75_   _85_   _95_   _105_   _115_

92   _102_   _112_   _122_   _132_   _142_

Closer To

(handwritten at top: 23 −10 / 13; 13 ←10 / 0̄3̄ *)*

☐ Write **0** or **10**.

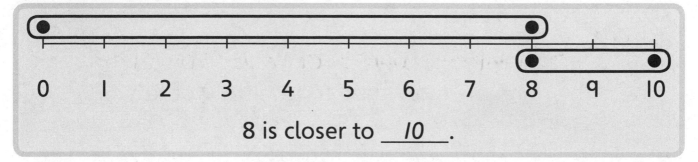

8 is closer to __10__.

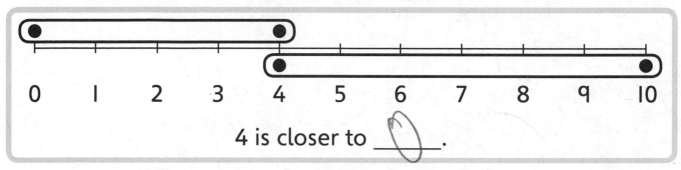

4 is closer to __0__.

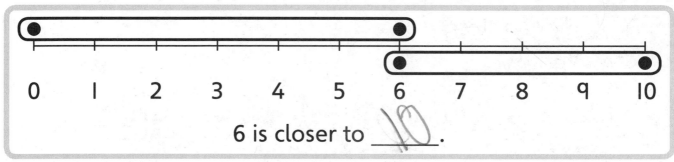

6 is closer to __10__.

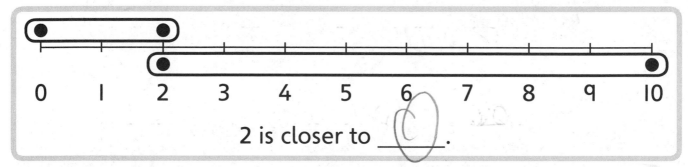

2 is closer to __0__.

☐ **Bonus:** Show the number that is **equally** close to 0 and 10.

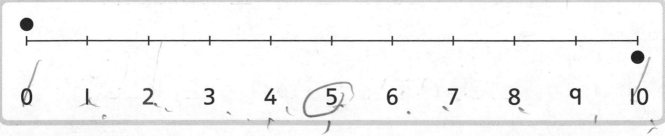

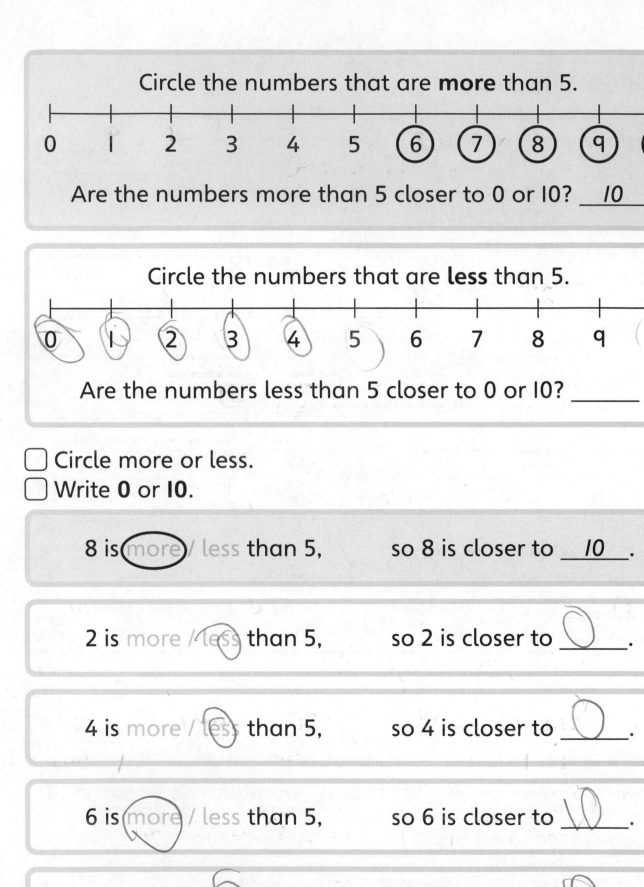

Circle the numbers that are **more** than 5.

0 I 2 3 4 5 ⑥ ⑦ ⑧ ⑨ ⑩

Are the numbers more than 5 closer to 0 or 10? __10__

Circle the numbers that are **less** than 5.

⓪ ① ② ③ ④ 5 6 7 8 9 10

Are the numbers less than 5 closer to 0 or 10? _____

☐ Circle more or less.
☐ Write **0** or **10**.

8 is (more) / less than 5,   so 8 is closer to __10__.

2 is more / (less) than 5,   so 2 is closer to __0__.

4 is more / (less) than 5,   so 4 is closer to __0__.

6 is (more) / less than 5,   so 6 is closer to __10__.

I is more / (less) than 5,   so I is closer to __0__.

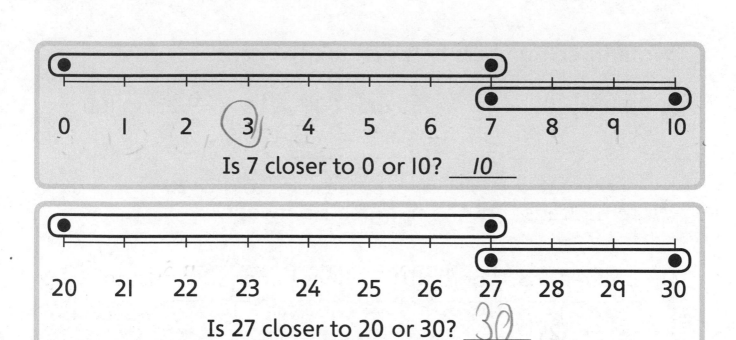

Is 7 closer to 0 or 10? __10__

Is 27 closer to 20 or 30? _30_

Is 57 closer to 50 or 60? _60_

☐ Circle the correct number.

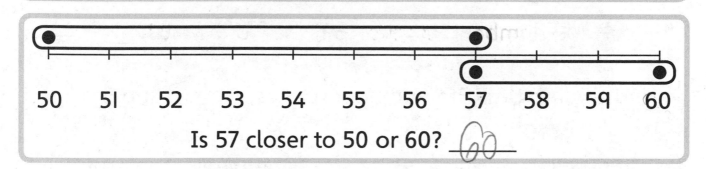

Is 87 closer to 80 or **90**?

Is 97 closer to 90 or **100**?

Is 3 closer to **0** or 10?

Is 13 closer to **10** or 20?

Is 73 closer to **70** or 80?

Is 9 closer to 0 or **10**?

Is 29 closer to 20 or **30**?

Is 99 closer to 90 or **100**?

Is 46 closer to 40 or **50**?

Is 24 closer to **20** or 30?

Is 52 closer to **50** or 60?

Is 38 closer to 30 or **40**?

☐ Write three numbers between the two tens.

20 and 30	50 and 60	90 and 100
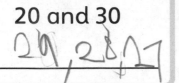	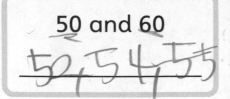	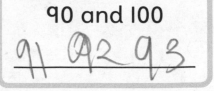

☐ Write the tens that the number is between.

34 is between __30__ and __40__ .

86 is between __80__ and __90__.

41 is between __40__ and __50__.

65 is between __60__ and __70__.

☐ Find the ten that the number is closest to by using 5.

37 is between __30__ and __40__ .

7 is (more) / less than 5.

37 is closest to __40__ .

62 is between __60__ and __70__.

2 is more / (less) than 5.

62 is closest to __60__.

26 is between __20__ and __30__.

6 is (more) / less than 5.

26 is closest to __30__

84 is between __80__ and __90__.

4 is more / (less) than 5.

84 is closest to __80__.

53 is closest to __50__

79 is closest to __80__ .

Estimating Numbers

10 dots are circled.

☐ Estimate the closest ten.
☐ Group by 10s to check.

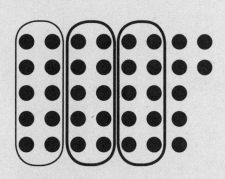

Estimate: ___30___

Check: ___37___

Closest ten: ___40___

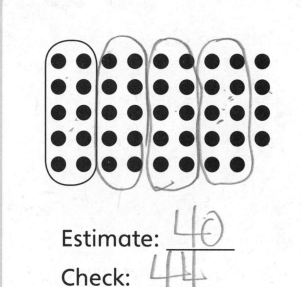

Estimate: ___40___

Check: ___44___

Closest ten: ___40___

Estimate: ___30___

Check: ___36___

Closest ten: ___40___

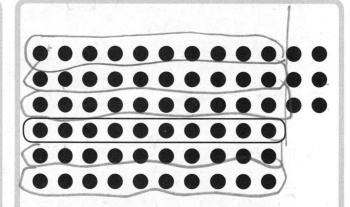

Estimate: ___60___

Check: ___66___

Closest ten: ___70___

10 dots are circled.

☐ Estimate the closest ten. _____

☐ Circle 2 more groups of 10. Estimate again. _____

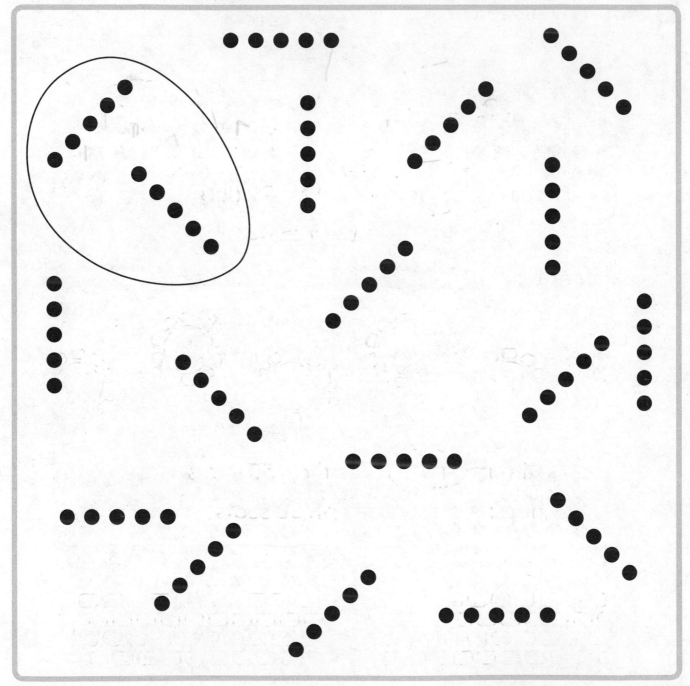

☐ Group by 10s to count. _____

Did circling more groups of 10 improve your estimate? yes / no

☐ Why do you think that happened?

Estimating Using Benchmarks

☐ Estimate.
☐ Make groups of 5 or 10 to check.

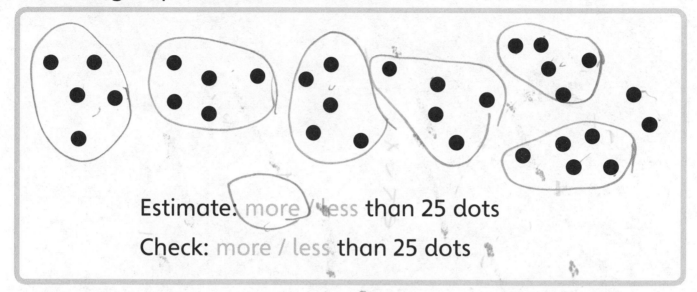

Estimate: <u>more</u> / less than 25 dots

Check: more / less than 25 dots

Estimate: (more) / less than 50 seats

Check: more / less than 50 seats

Estimate: more / less than 100 seats

Check: more / less than 100 seats

☐ Use your fist to cover some beans.
☐ Circle the group you covered.
☐ Fill in the blanks.

How many beans in one group? _____

About how many groups? _____

How many beans altogether? _____

Estimate: _____

Count: _____

Even and Odd

The number of stars is **even** if you can pair them up.
The number of stars is **odd** if you cannot.

☐ Count the stars.
☐ Circle pairs.
☐ Write **even** or **odd**.

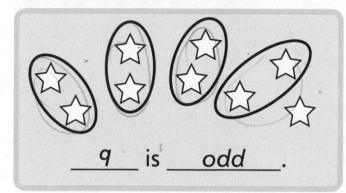

___9___ is ___odd___.

___11___ is ___odd___.

___14___ is ___even___.

___15___ is ___odd___.

___14___ is ___even___.

___17___ is ___odd___.

☐ Write **even** if you can make 2 equal teams.
Write **odd** if you cannot.

8 is ___even___.

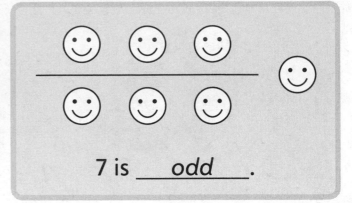

7 is ___odd___.

6 is ___even___.

3 is ___odd___.

_4_ is ___even___.

_5_ is ___odd___.

_13_ is ___odd___.

_12_ is ___even___.

_11_ is ___odd___.

Patterns with Even and Odd

☐ Pair objects up.
☐ Write **even** or **odd**.

 1 is _Odd_.

 2 is _even_.

 3 is _Odd_.

 4 is _even_.

 5 is _Odd_.

 6 is _even_.

 7 is _Odd_.

 8 is _even_.

 9 is _Odd_.

☐ Write **O** for odd and **E** for even.
☐ Extend both patterns.

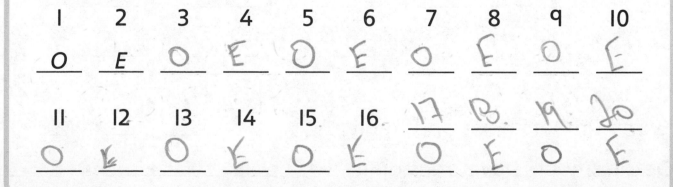

1	2	3	4	5	6	7	8	9	10
O	E	O	E	O	E	O	E	O	E

11	12	13	14	15	16	17	18	19	20
O	E	O	E	O	E	O	E	O	E

☐ Shade the even numbers.
☐ Circle the odd numbers.

1	2	3	4	5	6	7	8	9	10
11	12	13	14	15	16	17	18	19	20

☐ Write the **ones digits** of the **shaded** numbers.
☐ Extend the pattern.

___ ___ ___ ___ ___

___ ___ ___ ___ ___

___ ___ ___ ___ ___

☐ Write the **ones digits** of the **circled** numbers.
☐ Extend the pattern.

___ ___ ___ ___ ___

___ ___ ___ ___ ___

___ ___ ___ ___ ___

Even numbers have ones digit ____, ____, ____, ____, or ____.

Odd numbers have ones digit ____, ____, ____, ____, or ____.

Even numbers have ones digit 0, 2, 4, 6, or 8.
Odd numbers have ones digit 1, 3, 5, 7, or 9.

☐ Circle the even numbers.
☐ Underline the odd numbers.

1   2   3   4   5   6   7   8   9   10

2   4   6   8   10   12   14   16   18   20

5   10   15   20   25   30   35   40   45   50

10   20   30   40   50   60   70   80   90   100

4   26   47
17   94   61
17
43
3   71
9   34
94   90
26
81   18   62

☐ **Bonus:** Describe all the patterns you see.

☐ Write the next even number.

56 _____	60 _____	74 _____	12 _____
36 _____	46 _____	52 _____	70 _____

☐ Write the next odd number.

57 _____	61 _____	75 _____	33 _____
25 _____	47 _____	23 _____	91 _____

☐ Write the even number before.

_____ 26	_____ 14	_____ 38	_____ 42
_____ 78	_____ 84	_____ 12	_____ 56

☐ Write the odd number before.

_____ 79	_____ 53	_____ 65	_____ 83
_____ 55	_____ 85	_____ 99	_____ 47

Patterns in Adding

☐ Separate.
☐ Write the number in different ways.

$6 = 1 + \underline{5}$
$6 = 2 + \underline{4}$
$6 = 3 + \underline{3}$

$10 = 1 + \underline{}$
$10 = 2 + \underline{}$
$10 = 3 + \underline{}$
$10 = 4 + \underline{}$
$10 = 5 + \underline{}$

$7 = 1 + \underline{}$
$7 = 2 + \underline{}$
$7 = 3 + \underline{}$

$8 = 1 + \underline{}$
$8 = 2 + \underline{}$
$8 = 3 + \underline{}$
$8 = 4 + \underline{}$

☐ Write 9 in different ways.

$9 = \underline{} + \underline{}$

$9 = \underline{} + \underline{}$

$9 = \underline{} + \underline{}$

$9 = \underline{} + \underline{}$

Adding Tens and Ones

☐ Write the number as a sum of 10s and 1s.

32 = _10 + 10 + 10 + 1 + 1_

13 = _10 + 1 + 1 + 1_

41 = _10 + 10 + 10 + 10 + 1 = 41_

22 = _10 + 10 + 2 = 22_

☐ We can write 24 = 20 + 4. Write the number in the same way.

35 = _30 + 5_

47 = _____

63 = _____

81 = _____

56 = _____

92 = _____

☐ Add.

40 + 5 = _45_

6 + 20 = _____

70 + 1 = _____

8 + 60 = _____

70 + 7 = _____

4 + 50 = _____

30 + 8 = _____

9 + 10 = _____

6 + 80 = _____

7 + 90 = _____

9 + 70 = _____

90 + 9 = _____

☐ Add.

5 + 2 =   1 + 1 + 1 + 1 + 1   +   1 + 1   = _____

50 + 20 =   10 + 10 + 10 + 10 + 10   +   10 + 10   = _____

4 + 4 =   1 + 1 + 1 + 1   +   1 + 1 + 1 + 1   = _____

40 + 40 =   10 + 10 + 10 + 10   +   10 + 10 + 10 + 10   = _____

2 + 3 =   1 + 1   +   1 + 1 + 1   = _____

20 + 30 =   10 + 10   +   10 + 10 + 10   = _____

2 + 6 = _____

20 + 60 = _____

4 + 1 = _____

40 + 10 = _____

5 + 4 = _____

50 + 40 = _____

1 + 5 = _____

10 + 50 = _____

3 + 3 = _____

30 + 30 = _____

3 + 4 = _____

30 + 40 = _____

1 + 3 + 2 = _____

10 + 30 + 20 = _____

2 + 3 + 2 + 1 = _____

20 + 30 + 20 + 10 = _____

Adding in Two Ways

☐ Move the line one dot to the right. →
☐ Write the new addition sentence.

● ● | ● ● ● ● $2 + 4 = 6$

● ● ● | ● ● ● $\underline{3 + 3 = 6}$

● | ● ● ● ● $1 + 4 = 5$

● ● ● ● ●   _____

● ● ● | ● ● $3 + 2 = 5$

● ● ● ● ●   _____

● ● ● ● | ● ● $4 + 2 = 6$

● ● ● ● ● ●   _____

● ● | ● ● $2 + 2 = 4$

● ● ● ●   _____

● | ● ● $1 + 2 = 3$

● ● ●   _____

| ● ● ● ● $0 + 4 = 4$

● ● ● ●   _____

● ● ● | ● $3 + 1 = 4$

● ● ● ●   _____

How does the first number change? _*It goes up by 1.*_

How does the second number change? _____

What happens to the total? _____

☐ Why does that happen?

☐ Add and subtract I to make a new number sentence.

2 + 5 = 7

+1 ↓   ↓ −1

3 + 4 = 7

---

3 + 8 = 11

+1 ↓   ↓ −1

☐ + ☐ = ☐

---

6 + 3 = 9

+1 ↓   ↓ −1

☐ + ☐ = ☐

---

8 + 3 = 11

+1 ↓   ↓ −1

☐ + ☐ = ☐

---

9 + 6 = 15

+1 ↓   ↓ __

☐ + ☐ = ☐

---

5 + 2 = 7

__ ↓   ↓ −1

☐ + ☐ = ☐

---

7 + 11 = 18

__ ↓   ↓ −1

☐ + ☐ = ☐

---

11 + 7 = 18

+1 ↓   ↓ __

☐ + ☐ = ☐

☐ Finish the addition sentence.

6 + 11 = 7 + _____

8 + 4 = 9 + _____

☐ Draw a model.
☐ Move the line one dot to the left. ←
☐ Write the new addition sentence.

● ●|● ● ● ●   2 + 4 = 6
●|● ● ● ● ●   _1 + 5 = 6_

● ●|● ● ●   2 + 3 = 5
_____

4 + 1 = 5
_____

4 + 2 = 6
_____

2 + 2 = 4
_____

1 + 2 = 3
_____

2 + 1 = 3
_____

4 + 0 = 4
_____

How does the first number change? _____

How does the second number change? _____

What happens to the total? _____

☐ Why does that happen?

☐ Change both numbers in opposite ways.
☐ Complete the two addition sentences.

13 + 4 = ☐17☐
−3 ↓   ↓ +3
☐10☐ + ☐7☐ = ☐17☐

8 + 7 = ☐15☐
+2 ↓   ↓ −2
☐ + ☐ = ☐

7 + 8 = ☐
+3 ↓   ↓ __
☐ + ☐ = ☐

11 + 7 = ☐
−1 ↓   ↓ __
☐ + ☐ = ☐

12 + 6 = ☐
−2 ↓   ↓ __
☐ + ☐ = ☐

5 + 13 = ☐
__ ↓   ↓ −3
☐ + ☐ = ☐

11 + 7 = ☐
__ ↓   ↓ +3
☐ + ☐ = ☐

9 + 8 = ☐
+1 ↓   ↓ __
☐ + ☐ = ☐

In each question, did the total change? _____

Using 10 to Add

☐ Use the group of 10 to help you add.

7 6

7 + 6 = 10 + 3 = 13

8 6

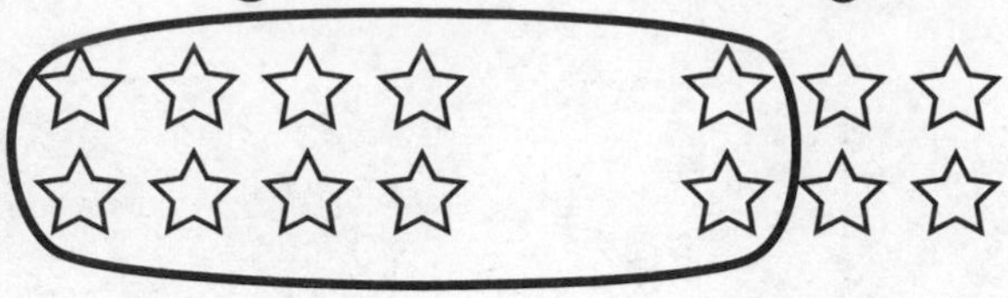

8 + 6 = 10 + ____ = ____

9 7

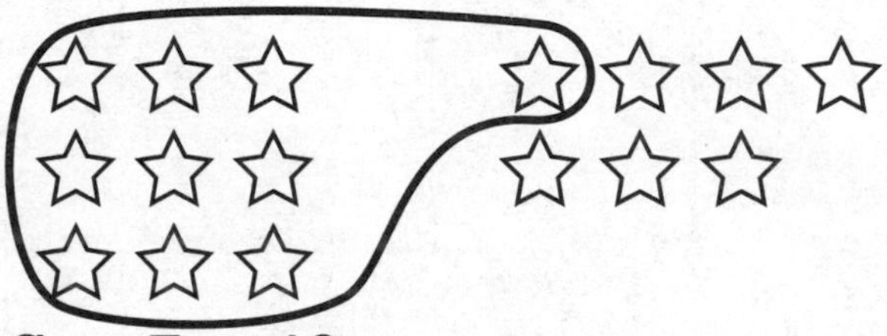

9 + 7 = 10 + ____ = ____

8 8

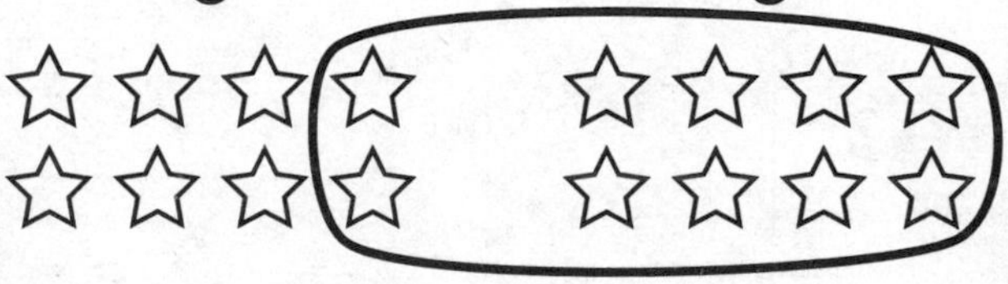

8 + 8 = ____ + 10 = ____

7 5

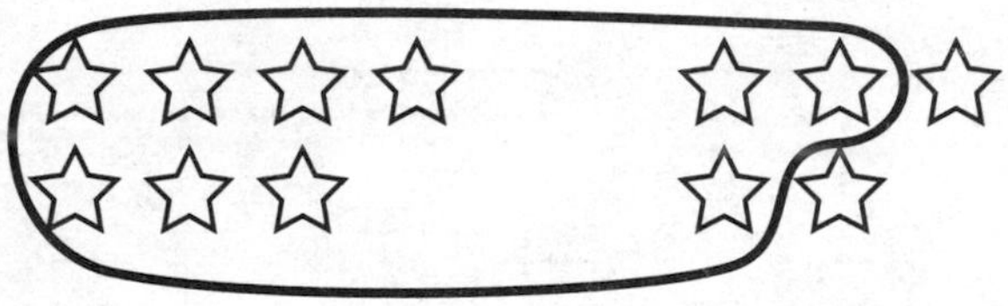

7 + 5 = 10 + ____ = ____

4 8

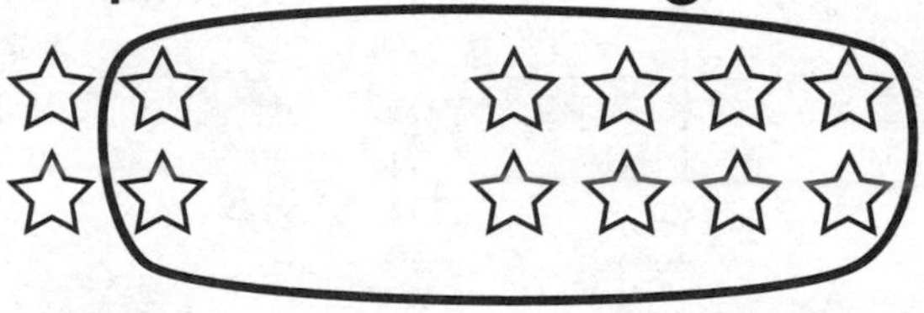

4 + 8 = ____ + 10 = ____

☐ Sara groups 10 in two ways. Does she get the same answer?

3 9

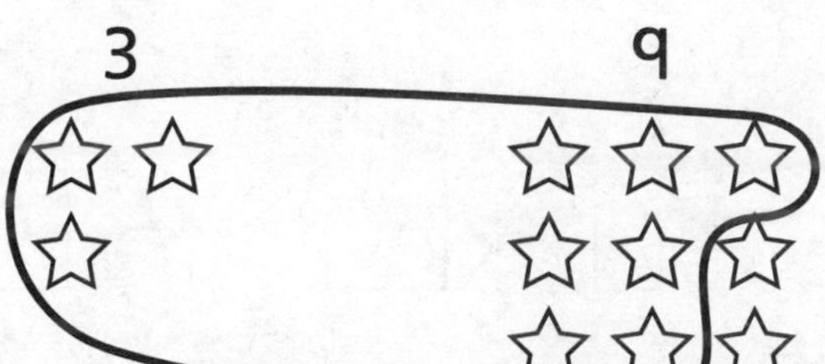

3 + 9 = 10 + ____ = ____

3 9

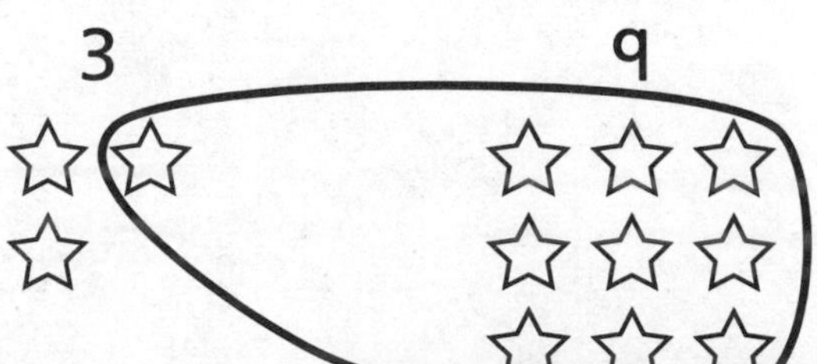

3 + 9 = ____ + 10 = ____

☐ Circle a group of 10.
☐ Use 10 to add.

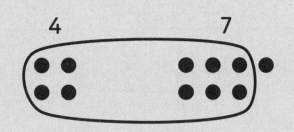

4 + 7 = 10 + __1__ = __11__

8 + 6 = 10 + ____ = ____

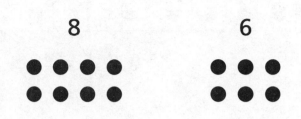

9 + 4 = 10 + ____ = ____

9 + 2 = 10 + ____ = ____

7 + 7 = 10 + ____ = ____

Make your own.

Using the Nearest 10 to Add

◻ Use 10 to add.

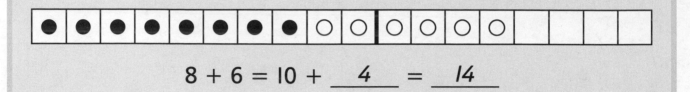

$8 + 6 = 10 + \underline{\quad4\quad} = \underline{\quad14\quad}$

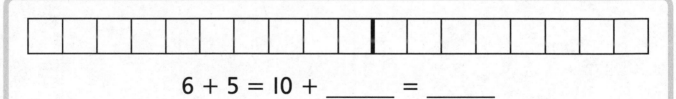

$7 + 5 = 10 + \underline{\qquad} = \underline{\qquad}$

$7 + 9 = 10 + \underline{\qquad} = \underline{\qquad}$

◻ Draw the circles, then add.

$6 + 5 = 10 + \underline{\qquad} = \underline{\qquad}$

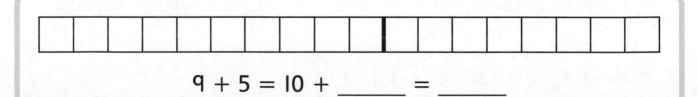

$9 + 5 = 10 + \underline{\qquad} = \underline{\qquad}$

Does using 10 make adding easier? \underline{\qquad}

▨ Explain.

▨ Which two answers are the same? Why did that happen?

Number Sense 2-54

☐ What makes 10 with the first number?
Subtract that amount from the second number.
☐ Complete the addition sentences.

8 + 5 = 13
+2 ↓   ↓ −2
10 + 3 = 13

8 + 7 = ☐
___ ↓   ↓ ___
☐ + ☐ = ☐

9 + 6 = ☐
___ ↓   ↓ ___
☐ + ☐ = ☐

9 + 8 = ☐
___ ↓   ↓ ___
☐ + ☐ = ☐

8 + 9 = ☐
___ ↓   ↓ ___
☐ + ☐ = ☐

9 + 7 = ☐
___ ↓   ↓ ___
☐ + ☐ = ☐

9 + 5 = 10 + ___ = ___

8 + 4 = 10 + ___ = ___

9 + 4 = ___ + ___ = ___

8 + 6 = ___ + ___ = ___

☐ Add I to one of the numbers.
☐ Subtract I from the other number.
☐ Complete the new addition sentence.

32 + 9
= __31__ + __10__ = __41__

19 + 8
= ____ + ____ = ____

7 + 29
= ____ + ____ = ____

27 + 19
= ____ + ____ = ____

19 + 16
= ____ + ____ = ____

29 + 6
= ____ + ____ = ____

18 + 9
= ____ + ____ = ____

9 + 36
= ____ + ____ = ____

9 + 47
= ____ + ____ = ____

38 + 19
= ____ + ____ = ____

▤ Sam has to solve 27 + 29. He says 26 + 30 has the same answer. Explain why he is correct.

▤ Which problem is easier, 27 + 29 or 26 + 30? Explain.

☐ Make a new addition problem by adding and subtracting 2.
☐ Solve the new addition problem.

$18 + 15$

$= \underline{\quad 20 \quad} + \underline{\quad\quad} = \underline{\quad\quad}$

$14 + 28$

$= \underline{\quad\quad} + \underline{\quad 30 \quad} = \underline{\quad\quad}$

$37 + 48$

$= \underline{\quad\quad} + \underline{\quad 50 \quad} = \underline{\quad\quad}$

$68 + 24$

$= \underline{\quad 70 \quad} + \underline{\quad\quad} = \underline{\quad\quad}$

$42 + 54$

$= \underline{\quad 40 \quad} + \underline{\quad\quad} = \underline{\quad\quad}$

$72 + 17$

$= \underline{\quad 70 \quad} + \underline{\quad\quad} = \underline{\quad\quad}$

$56 + 32$

$= \underline{\quad\quad} + \underline{\quad\quad} = \underline{\quad\quad}$

$28 + 45$

$= \underline{\quad\quad} + \underline{\quad\quad} = \underline{\quad\quad}$

$22 + 35$

$= \underline{\quad\quad} + \underline{\quad\quad} = \underline{\quad\quad}$

$43 + 48$

$= \underline{\quad\quad} + \underline{\quad\quad} = \underline{\quad\quad}$

Using Tens and Ones to Add

How many tens and ones altogether?

☐ Add.

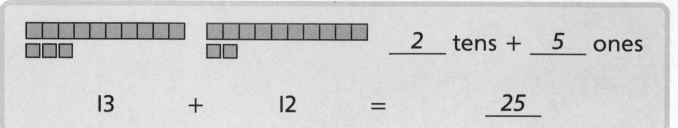

_____2___ tens + ___5___ ones

13   +   12   =   __25__

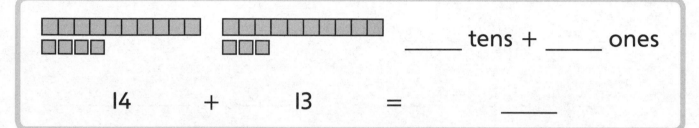

_____ tens + _____ ones

14   +   13   =   ____

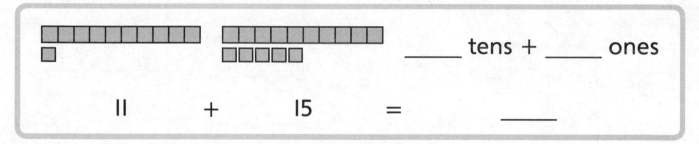

_____ tens + _____ ones

11   +   15   =   ____

☐ Now draw the blocks and add.

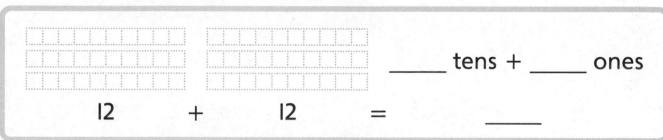

_____ tens + _____ ones

12   +   12   =   ____

☐ Make your own problem.

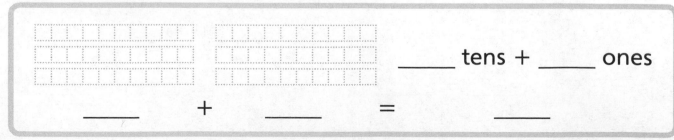

_____ tens + _____ ones

____   +   ____   =   ____

☐ Add by separating the tens and ones.

23 = 20 + 3
+ 34 = 30 + 4
[57] ← 50 + 7

34 = 30 + 4
+ 15 = 10 + 5
☐ ← 40 + 9

27 = 20 + ☐
+ 22 = 20 + ☐
☐ ← 40 + ☐

35 = ☐ + ☐
+ 42 = ☐ + ☐
☐ ← ☐ + ☐

15 = ☐ + ☐
+ 23 = ☐ + ☐
☐ ← ☐ + ☐

26 = ☐ + ☐
+ 13 = ☐ + ☐
☐ ← ☐ + ☐

34 = ☐ + ☐
+ 54 = ☐ + ☐
☐ ← ☐ + ☐

26 = ☐ + ☐
+ 33 = ☐ + ☐
☐ ← ☐ + ☐

22 = ☐ + ☐
14 ☐ + ☐
+ 21 = ☐ + ☐
☐ ← ☐ + ☐

11 = ☐ + ☐
22 ☐ + ☐
+ 33 = ☐ + ☐
☐ ← ☐ + ☐

Add by using a tens and ones chart.

35 + 32

tens	ones
3	5
3	2
6	7

→ 67

24 + 41

tens	ones
2	4
4	1

→ □

46 + 31

tens	ones

→ □

43 + 23

tens	ones

→ □

27 + 21 + 51

tens	ones

→ □

31 + 42 + 14

tens	ones

→ □

tens	ones
3	2
+ 2	7

tens	ones
4	8
+ 3	1

tens	ones
5	5
+ 2	3

tens	ones
2	2
+ 1	3

37 + 22   63 + 16   25 + 34   31 + 62   54 + 34   23 + 43

Many Ways to Write a Number

☐ Write 53 in many ways.

1	2	3	4	5	6	7	8	9	10
11	12	13	14	15	16	17	18	19	20
21	22	23	24	25	26	27	28	29	30
31	32	33	34	35	36	37	38	39	40
41	42	43	44	45	46	47	48	49	50
51	52	53	54	55	56	57	58	59	60

___5___ tens + ___3___ ones

1	2	3	4	5	6	7	8	9	10
11	12	13	14	15	16	17	18	19	20
21	22	23	24	25	26	27	28	29	30
31	32	33	34	35	36	37	38	39	40
41	42	43	44	45	46	47	48	49	50
51	52	53	54	55	56	57	58	59	60

_____ tens + _____ ones

1	2	3	4	5	6	7	8	9	10
11	12	13	14	15	16	17	18	19	20
21	22	23	24	25	26	27	28	29	30
31	32	33	34	35	36	37	38	39	40
41	42	43	44	45	46	47	48	49	50
51	52	53	54	55	56	57	58	59	60

_____ tens + _____ ones

☐ Write the number in many ways.

24

tens	ones
2	4
I	14
0	24

27

tens	ones

26

tens	ones

37

tens	ones

38

tens	ones

31

tens	ones

50

tens	ones

56

tens	ones

52

tens	ones

Regrouping

☐ Group 10 ones blocks together.
☐ Add.

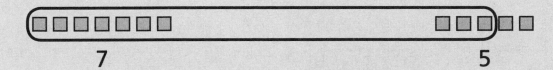

7   5

$$7 + 5 = 10 + \underline{\quad 2 \quad} = \underline{\quad 12 \quad}$$

6   8

$$6 + 8 = 10 + \underline{\qquad} = \underline{\qquad}$$

5   8

$$5 + 8 = 10 + \underline{\qquad} = \underline{\qquad}$$

8   4

$$8 + 4 = 10 + \underline{\qquad} = \underline{\qquad}$$

7   7

$$7 + 7 = 10 + \underline{\qquad} = \underline{\qquad}$$

☐ Group 10 ones blocks together.
How many tens and ones?
☐ Add.

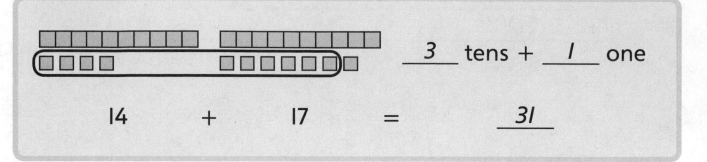

_____3_____ tens + _____1_____ one

14   +   17   =   ___31___

_____ tens + _____ ones

17   +   16   =   _____

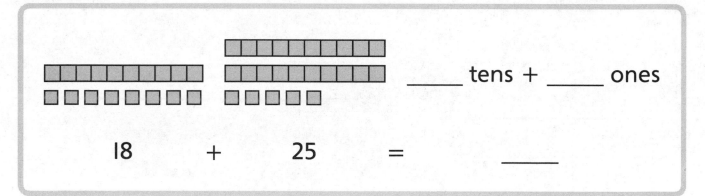

_____ tens + _____ ones

18   +   25   =   _____

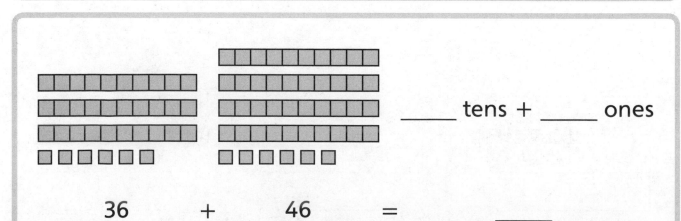

_____ tens + _____ ones

36   +   46   =   _____

☐ Trade groups of 10 ones for tens.
☐ Regroup in the next row.

tens	ones
4	27
6	7

tens	ones
3	12

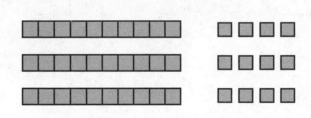

tens	ones
5	21

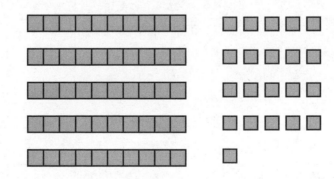

tens	ones
3	15

tens	ones
6	19

tens	ones
4	28

☐ Add the tens and ones.
☐ Regroup in the next row.
☐ Write the answer.

tens	ones
1	6
5	5
6	11
7	1

16
+ 55
[71]

tens	ones
1	2
2	9

12
+ 29
☐

tens	ones
2	5
3	8

25
+ 38
☐

tens	ones
5	7
2	6

57
+ 26
☐

tens	ones
2	8
2	6

28
+ 26
☐

tens	ones
2	3
5	2
1	6

23
52
+ 16
☐

The Standard Algorithm for Addition

☐ Add the ones.
☐ Write the tens digit in the tens column.
☐ Write the ones digit in the ones column.

$5 + 9 = \boxed{1}\,\boxed{4}$

```
   tens ones
    [1]
     1   5
  +  2   9
  _____
    [ ]  [4]
```

$3 + 8 = \boxed{1}\,\boxed{1}$

```
   tens ones
    [ ]
     2   3
  +  3   8
  _____
    [ ]  [ ]
```

$6 + 4 = \boxed{1}\,\boxed{0}$

```
   tens ones
    [ ]
     5   6
  +  3   4
  _____
    [ ]  [ ]
```

$7 + 5 = \boxed{}\,\boxed{}$

```
   tens ones
    [ ]
     3   7
  +  2   5
  _____
    [ ]  [ ]
```

$6 + 9 = \boxed{}\,\boxed{}$

```
   tens ones
    [ ]
     1   6
  +  4   9
  _____
    [ ]  [ ]
```

$\_ + \_ = \boxed{}\,\boxed{}$

```
   tens ones
    [ ]
     2   7
  +  3   8
  _____
    [ ]  [ ]
```

```
    [ ]
     1   4
  +  3   8
  _____
    [ ]  [ ]
```

```
    [ ]
     4   7
  +  2   3
  _____
    [ ]  [ ]
```

```
    [ ]
     1   5
  +  3   5
  _____
    [ ]  [ ]
```

☐ Add the ones first.
☐ Then add the tens to find the total.

☐ **1** 1 5 + 2 9 ——— ☐4☐ 4	☐ 2 3 + 3 8 ——— ☐ ☐
☐ 5 6 + 3 4 ——— ☐ ☐	☐ 2 9 + 1 1 ——— ☐ ☐
☐ 3 7 + 2 5 ——— ☐ ☐	☐ 1 6 + 4 9 ——— ☐ ☐
☐ 2 7 + 3 8 ——— ☐ ☐	☐ 1 5 + 1 9 ——— ☐ ☐
☐ 1 4 + 3 8 ——— ☐ ☐	☐ 4 7 + 2 3 ——— ☐ ☐
☐ 1 5 + 3 5 ——— ☐ ☐	☐ 2 8 + 3 8 ——— ☐ ☐

☐ Add. Regroup when you need to.

	1	
	1	9
+	2	6
	4	5

	☐	
	2	5
+	3	3
	5	8

	☐	
	3	7
+	2	5
	☐	☐

	☐	
	2	3
+	4	6
	☐	☐

	☐	
	2	9
+		4
	☐	☐

	☐	
	1	3
+	2	2
	☐	☐

	☐	
	4	7
+		3
	☐	☐

	☐	
	8	6
+		1
	☐	☐

Liz added the tens before the ones.

☐ Circle the answers she got wrong.

	☐	
	1	1
+	5	8
	6	9

	1	
	1	7
+	2	7
	3	4

	1	
	2	6
+	2	6
	4	2

	☐	
	4	3
+	2	5
	6	8

☐ Add.

29 + 14   37 + 46   48 + 23   55 + 39

Doubles

☐ Draw the same number of dots on the other side.
☐ Write a doubles sentence.

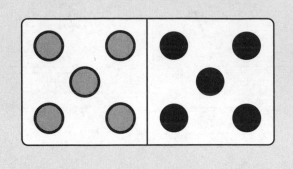

___10___ is double ___5___

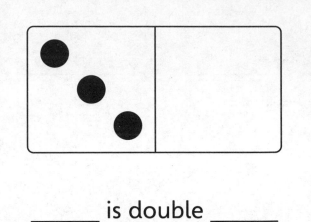

_____ is double _____

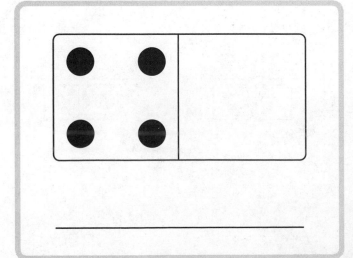

_____ is double _____

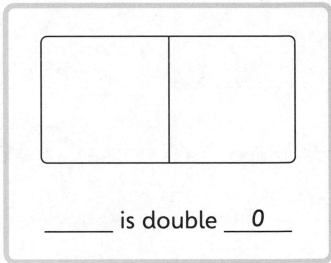

_____ is double ___0___

_____

_____

46

☐ Write an addition sentence for the double.

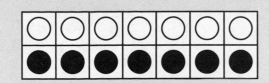

_____7_____ + _____7_____ = _____14_____

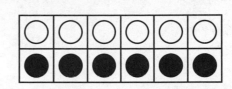

_____ + _____ = _____

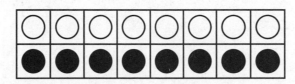

_____ + _____ = _____

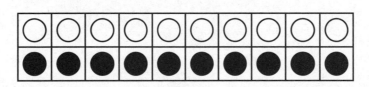

_____ + _____ = _____

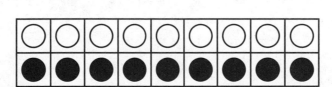

_____ + _____ = _____

_____ + _____ = 2   _____ + _____ = 8

COPYRIGHT © 2017 JUMP MATH: NOT TO BE COPIED

Number Sense 2-59   47

Using Doubles to Add

☐ Double, then add 1.

$4 + 4 = \underline{8}$

so $4 + 5 = \underline{9}$

$3 + 3 = \underline{}$

so $4 + 3 = \underline{}$

$7 + 7 = \underline{}$

so $8 + 7 = \underline{}$

$8 + 8 = \underline{}$

so $8 + 9 = \underline{}$

$6 + 6 = \underline{}$

so $6 + 7 = \underline{}$

$5 + 5 = \underline{}$

so $6 + 5 = \underline{}$

$\underline{} + \underline{} = \underline{}$

so $\qquad 7 + 8 = \underline{}$

$\underline{} + \underline{} = \underline{}$

so $\qquad 5 + 4 = \underline{}$

$\underline{} + \underline{} = \underline{}$

so $\qquad 5 + 6 = \underline{}$

$\underline{} + \underline{} = \underline{}$

so $\qquad 10 + 9 = \underline{}$

Bonus

☐ Find $30 + 31$.

◯ Double, then subtract I.

$7 + 7 = \underline{14}$

so $7 + 6 = \underline{13}$

$9 + 9 = \underline{}$

so $8 + 9 = \underline{}$

$6 + 6 = \underline{}$

so $6 + 5 = \underline{}$

$8 + 8 = \underline{}$

so $7 + 8 = \underline{}$

$8 + 8 = \underline{}$

so $8 + 7 = \underline{}$

$5 + 5 = \underline{}$

so $4 + 5 = \underline{}$

$\underline{} + \underline{} = \underline{}$

so $\quad 9 + 10 = \underline{}$

$\underline{} + \underline{} = \underline{}$

so $\quad 9 + 8 = \underline{}$

$\underline{} + \underline{} = \underline{}$

so $\quad 3 + 4 = \underline{}$

$\underline{} + \underline{} = \underline{}$

so $\quad 7 + 8 = \underline{}$

Bonus

▤ Find $40 + 39$.

☐ Write how many **more** or **less**.
☐ Find the double.
☐ Add.

4 + 5 is _____*I more than*_____ 4 + 4

4 + 4 = __8__   so   4 + 5 = __9__

8 + 9 is _____ 9 + 9

9 + 9 = _____   so   8 + 9 = _____

8 + 7 is _____ 8 + 8

8 + 8 = _____   so   8 + 7 = _____

6 + 7 is _____ 6 + 6

6 + 6 = _____   so   6 + 7 = _____

9 + 10 is _____ 10 + 10

10 + 10 = _____   so   9 + 10 = _____

7 + 6 is _____

_____   so   7 + 6 = _____

☐ Which two questions have the same answer?
  Why did that happen?

Subtraction Strategies

☐ Count backwards to subtract.

6 – 1 = _____   0 1 2 3 4 5 6 7 8 9 10

7 – 2 = _____   0 1 2 3 4 5 6 7 8 9 10

8 – 3 = _____   0 1 2 3 4 5 6 7 8 9 10

☐ Count forwards to subtract.

8 – 5 = _____   0 1 2 3 4 5 6 7 8 9 10

9 – 6 = _____   0 1 2 3 4 5 6 7 8 9 10

10 – 7 = _____   0 1 2 3 4 5 6 7 8 9 10

☐ Take away the coloured circles to subtract.

10 – 2 = _____   ○ ○ ○ ○ ○ ○ ○ ○ ● ●

11 – 3 = _____   ○ ○ ○ ○ ○ ○ ○ ○ ● ● ●

12 – 4 = _____   ○ ○ ○ ○ ○ ○ ○ ○ ● ● ● ●

☐ Write 4 more subtraction sentences with the same answer.

_____   10 – 6 = 4   _____

_____   _____

☐ Circle the easiest problem to solve.

17 − 9	18 − 10	19 − 11	20 − 12

11 − 8	12 − 9	13 − 10	14 − 11

18 − 13	17 − 12	16 − 11	15 − 10

Explain your choices. _____

_____

☐ Make an easier problem with the same answer.
☐ Subtract.

13 − 8 = $\boxed{15}$ − 10 = ___5___

13 − 9 = ☐ − 10 = _____

16 − 9 = ☐ − 10 = _____

14 − 8 = ☐ − 10 = _____

17 − 8 = ☐ − 10 = _____

15 − 9 = ☐ − 10 = _____

12 − 9 = ☐ − 10 = _____

Bonus

24 − 18 = ☐ − 20 = _____

☐ Subtract.

13 − 3 = _____

10 11 12 13 14 15 16 17 18 19 20

23 − 3 = _____

20 21 22 23 24 25 26 27 28 29 30

33 − 3 = _____

30 31 32 33 34 35 36 37 38 39 40

43 − 3 = _____

73 − 3 = _____

63 − 3 = _____

82 − 2 = _____

67 − 7 = _____

54 − 4 = _____

91 − 1 = _____

85 − 5 = _____

76 − 6 = _____

89 − 9 = _____

50 − 0 = _____

28 − 8 = _____

74 − 4 = _____

68 − 8 = _____

41 − 1 = _____

☐ Write **more** or **less**.
☐ Subtract.

74 − 3 is 1 ___*more*___ than 73 − 3

73 − 3 = _70_   so   74 − 3 = _71_

84 − 5 is 1 ___*less*___ than 85 − 5

85 − 5 = _____   so   84 − 5 = _____

75 − 6 is 1 _____ than 76 − 6

76 − 6 = _____   so   75 − 6 = _____

57 − 6 is 1 _____ than 56 − 6

56 − 6 = _____   so   57 − 6 = _____

48 − 9 is 1 _____ than 49 − 9

49 − 9 = _____   so   48 − 9 = _____

☐ Solve 78 − 9 in two ways.
☐ **Bonus:** Solve 78 − 9 in a third way.

Number Sense 2-61

More Subtraction Strategies

☐ Count on to subtract.

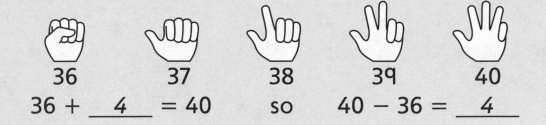

36   37   38   39   40

$36 + \underline{\ 4\ } = 40$ so $40 - 36 = \underline{\ 4\ }$

$7 + \underline{\qquad} = 10$ so $10 - 7 = \underline{\qquad}$

$17 + \underline{\qquad} = 20$ so $20 - 17 = \underline{\qquad}$

$27 + \underline{\qquad} = 30$ so $30 - 27 = \underline{\qquad}$

$10 - 8 = \underline{\qquad}$

$20 - 18 = \underline{\qquad}$

$30 - 28 = \underline{\qquad}$

$10 - 5 = \underline{\qquad}$

$20 - 15 = \underline{\qquad}$

$30 - 25 = \underline{\qquad}$

$10 - 9 = \underline{\qquad}$

$40 - 39 = \underline{\qquad}$

$90 - 89 = \underline{\qquad}$

---

4   5   6   7   40   50   60   70

$7 - 4 = 3$ so $70 - 40 = 3 \text{ tens} = 30$

$8 - 3 = \underline{\ 5\ }$ so $80 - 30 = \underline{\ 50\ }$

$10 - 5 = \underline{\qquad}$ so $100 - 50 = \underline{\qquad}$

$80 - 50 = \underline{\qquad}$ $70 - 30 = \underline{\qquad}$ $90 - 40 = \underline{\qquad}$

☐ Subtract by adding.

What is 80 − 56?

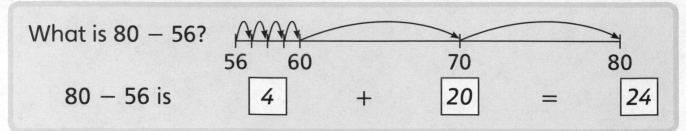

56   60   70   80

80 − 56 is $\boxed{4}$ + $\boxed{20}$ = $\boxed{24}$

What is 90 − 72?

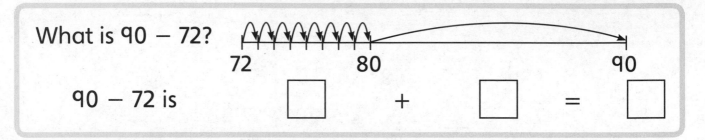

72   80   90

90 − 72 is   ☐   +   ☐   =   ☐

What is 83 − 40?

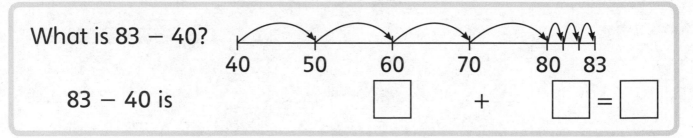

40   50   60   70   80 83

83 − 40 is   ☐   +   ☐ = ☐

What is 90 − 57?
57   60   90

90 − 57 is ☐ + ☐ = ☐

What is 75 − 40?
40   70   75

75 − 40 is ☐ + ☐ = ☐

What is 30 − 3?
3   10   30

30 − 3 is ☐ + ☐ = ☐

What is 64 − 20?
20   60   64

64 − 20 is ☐ + ☐ = ☐

What is 77 − 40?
40   70   77

77 − 40 is ☐ + ☐ = ☐

What is 80 − 16?
16   20   80

80 − 16 is ☐ + ☐ = ☐

☐ Subtract by using tens and adding.

$15 - 7 = \boxed{8} \leftarrow$

$7 \smile 10 \smile 15$

$\boxed{3} + \boxed{5} = \boxed{8}$

$25 - 17 = \boxed{} \leftarrow$

$17 \smile 20 \smile 25$

$\boxed{} + \boxed{} = \boxed{}$

$35 - 27 = \boxed{} \leftarrow$

$27 \smile 30 \smile 35$

$\boxed{} + \boxed{} = \boxed{}$

$42 - 36 = \boxed{} \leftarrow$

$36 \smile 40 \smile 42$

$\boxed{} + \boxed{} = \boxed{}$

$83 - 56 = \boxed{27} \leftarrow$

$56 \smile 60 \smile 80 \smile 83$

$\boxed{4} + \boxed{20} + \boxed{3} = \boxed{27}$

$92 - 49 = \boxed{} \leftarrow$

$49 \smile 50 \smile 90 \smile 92$

$\boxed{} + \boxed{} + \boxed{} = \boxed{}$

$78 - 29 = \boxed{} \leftarrow$

$29 \smile 30 \smile 70 \smile 78$

$\boxed{} + \boxed{} + \boxed{} = \boxed{}$

$95 - 57 = \boxed{} \leftarrow$

$57 \smile 60 \smile 90 \smile 95$

$\boxed{} + \boxed{} + \boxed{} = \boxed{}$

Subtracting Using Tens and Ones

☐ Use ones blocks and tens blocks to subtract.
☐ Colour blocks to show the second number.
   What number do the **white** blocks show?

47
− 23
[24]

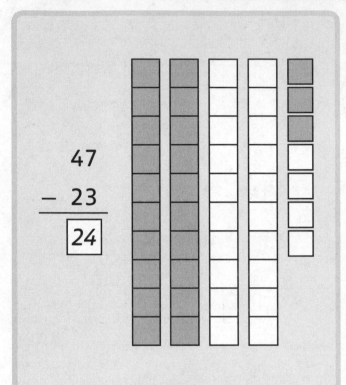

34
− 13
☐

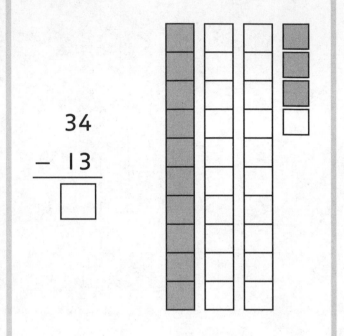

48
− 31
☐

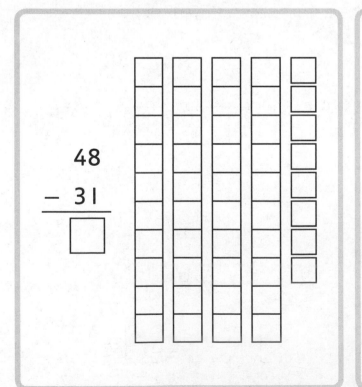

45
− 20
☐

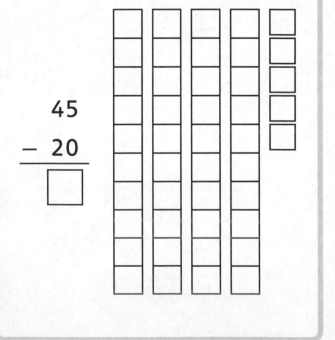

□ Cross out the correct number of 10s and 1s.
□ Subtract.

87
− 63
[24]

10̶ + 10̶ + 10̶ + 10̶ + 10̶ + 10̶ + 10 + 10
+1̶+1̶+1̶+ 1 + 1 + 1 + 1   )87

Cross out 6 tens and 3 ones. How much is left?

96
− 34
[ ]

10 + 10 + 10 + 10 + 10 + 10 + 10 + 10 + 10
+ 1 + 1 + 1 + 1 + 1 + 1   )96

Cross out 3 tens and 4 ones. How much is left?

57
− 31
[ ]

10 + 10 + 10 + 10 + 10
+ 1 + 1 + 1 + 1 + 1 + 1 + 1   )57

Cross out ____ tens and ____ one. How much is left?

28
− 11
[ ]

10 + 10
+ 1 + 1 + 1 + 1 + 1 + 1 + 1 + 1   )28

_____. How much is left?

65
− 34
[ ]

10 + 10 + 10 + 10 + 10 + 10
+ 1 + 1 + 1 + 1 + 1

34
+ [ ]
[ ]

Check by adding your answer. Do you get 65?

☐ Subtract.

8	5
− 4	2
4	3

8 tens 5 ones
− 4 tens 2 ones
⬜4⬜ tens ⬜3⬜ ones

6	7
− 2	5

6 tens 7 ones
− 2 tens 5 ones
⬜ tens ⬜ ones

9	7
− 2	1

9 tens 7 ones
− 2 tens 1 one
⬜ tens ⬜ ones

6	3
− 4	2

6 tens 3 ones
− 4 tens 2 ones
⬜ tens ⬜ ones

☐ Subtract, then check your answer by adding.

tens	ones
6	9
− 5	3

check
5	3
+	

tens	ones
8	5
− 3	1

check
3	1
+	

tens	ones
7	8
− 3	7

check
+	

tens	ones
6	9
− 2	4

check
+	

Regrouping for Subtraction

To find 45 − 28, Lela draws tens and ones blocks for 45. She tries to colour 28.

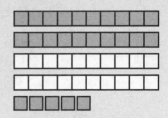

Lela can only colour 25, so she trades a tens block for 10 ones blocks. Now she can colour 28.

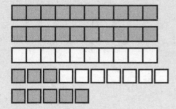

45 − 28 = 17
There are 17 left.

What number is shown?

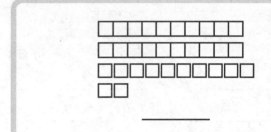

_____

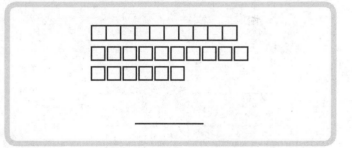

_____

☐ **Write the subtraction sentence for the model.**

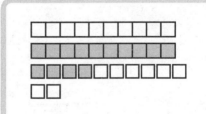

<u>32</u> − <u>14</u> = <u>18</u>

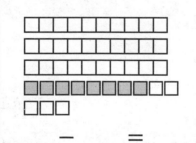

___ − ___ = ___

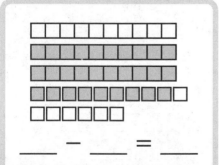

___ − ___ = ___

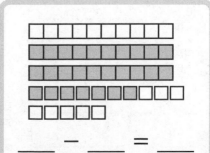

___ − ___ = ___

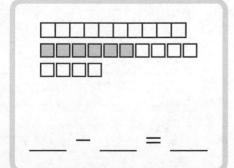

___ − ___ = ___

___ − ___ = ___

☐ Show Lela's trade in a tens and ones chart.

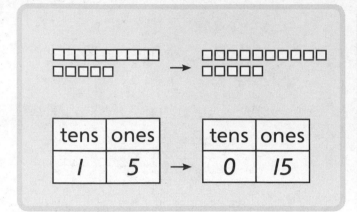

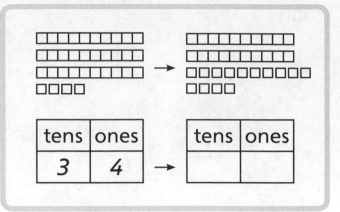

☐ Show Lela's subtraction using a tens and ones chart.

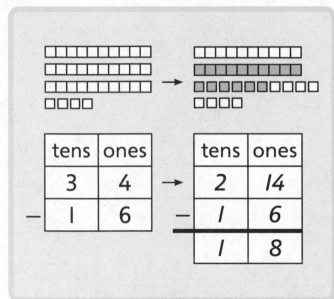

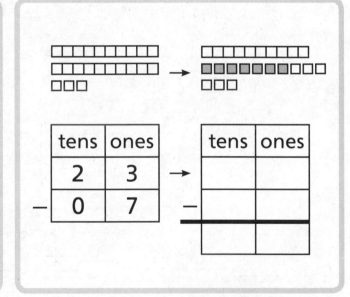

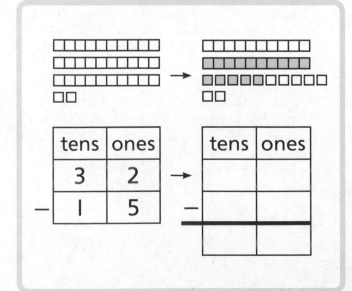

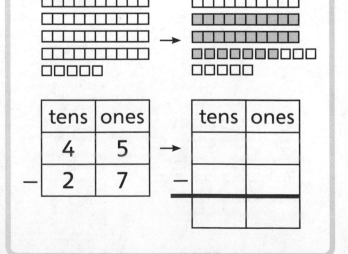

☐ Trade a ten for 10 ones.
☐ Subtract.
☐ Check your answer by adding.

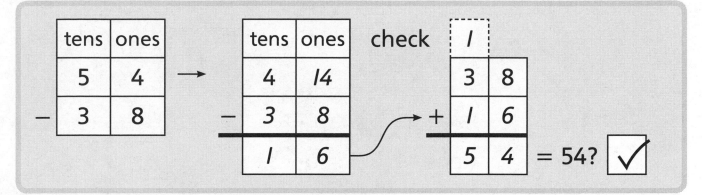

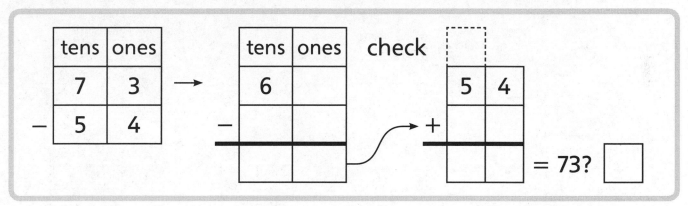

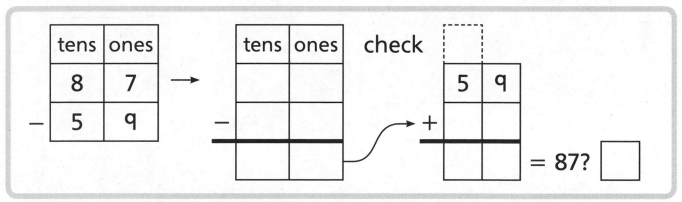

The Standard Algorithm for Subtraction

☐ Take 1 ten from the tens and add 10 ones to the ones.

50 = ___5___ tens + ___0___ ones

= ___4___ tens + ___10___ ones

73 = ___7___ tens + ___3___ ones

= _____ tens + _____ ones

85 = _____ tens + _____ ones

= _____ tens + _____ ones

☐ Regroup I ten as 10 ones. Subtract.

	6	15
	7̸	5̸
−	5	7
	1	8

	8	3
−	5	6

	5	4
−	3	9

	4	6
−	2	7

	9	2
−	8	7

	8	1
−	5	5

	5	3
−	2	9

	6	0
−	3	6

	9	1
−	7	2

	9	6
−	2	9

	8	7
−	3	8

	8	0
−	5	7

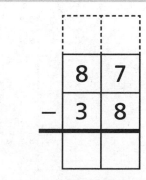 Check your answers by adding.

☐ Decide if you need to regroup. Subtract.

	4	8
−	2	5

	4	7
−	1	9

	4	9
−	1	7

	5	3
−	4	8

	5	8
−	4	3

	6	7
−	3	3

	5	8
−	2	6

	7	0
−	3	7

	8	1
−	6	1

	9	8
−	2	7

	8	5
−	3	6

	9	0
−	4	8

📓 Check your answers by adding.

Estimating Sums and Differences

☐ Write the closest ten.

| 38 _40_ | 61 _60_ | 59 _____ | 64 _____ |

| 93 _____ | 32 _____ | 87 _____ | 26 _____ |

☐ Use the closest tens to estimate the answer.

28 + 51

Estimate: _30 + 50 = 80_

37 + 29

Estimate: _____

42 + 19

Estimate: _____

27 + 73

Estimate: _____

11 + 81

Estimate: _____

49 + 18

Estimate: _____

9 + 28

Estimate: _____

59 + 21

Estimate: _____

☐ Use the closest tens to estimate the answer.

51 − 28
Estimate: __50 − 30 = 20__

47 − 29
Estimate: _____

82 − 19
Estimate: _____

73 − 17
Estimate: _____

91 − 11
Estimate: _____

59 − 18
Estimate: _____

☐ Estimate.
☐ Add or subtract to find the exact answer.

59 + 32

Estimate: _____

	5	9
+	3	2

71 − 28

Estimate: _____

	7	1
−	2	8

☐ Which is usually faster for adding and subtracting?
estimating / finding the exact answer

☐ Does estimating usually give the exact answer? yes / no

Growing Patterns

How many?

petals

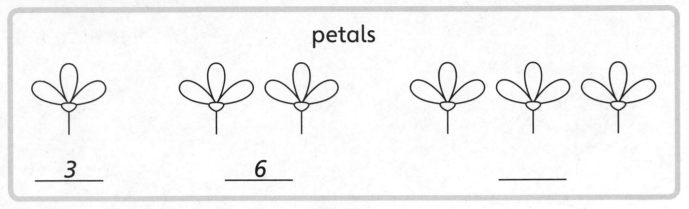

___3___   ___6___   _____

leaves

_____   _____   _____

wheels

_____   _____   _____

flower petals in each layer

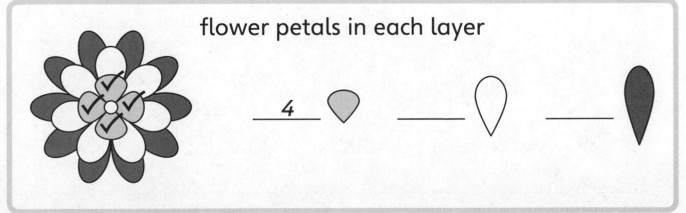

___4___   ___ ___   ___ ___

 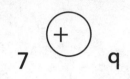 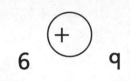

$\left(+2\right)$		$6 + 2 = 8$
6 8	6 7 8	8 is 2 more than 6.

☐ Write the number you add in the circles.

8 $\left(+I\right)$ 9	6 $\left(+\right)$ 9	7 $\left(+\right)$ 9	3 $\left(+\right)$ 7

2 $\left(+\right)$ 4	11 ◯ 13	10 ◯ 16	5 ◯ 8

4 ◯ 7	12 ◯ 18	10 ◯ 17	10 ◯ 20

2 ◯ 4 ◯ 6	5 ◯ 10 ◯ 15

15 ◯ 16 ◯ 17	8 ◯ 10 ◯ 12

8 ◯ 10 ◯ 12

 says the next number is 14. How does she know?

_____

Patterns and Algebra 2-7

makes patterns by adding the **same** number.

☐ Continue the pattern.

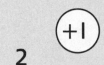 2 3 _4_   3 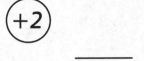 5 _____

 7 8 ◯ _____   2 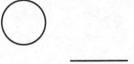 4 ◯ _____

3 13 ◯ _____   0 3 ◯ _____

☐ Find the number adds and continue the pattern.

5 ◯ 10 ◯ _____   1 ◯ 3 ◯ _____

4 ◯ 14 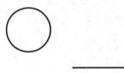◯ ◯ _____ ◯ _____ ◯ _____

7 ◯ 9 ◯ ◯ _____ ◯ _____ 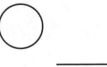◯ _____

20 ◯ 25 ◯ ◯ _____ ◯ _____ ◯ _____

Shrinking Patterns

How many?

pieces of pizza

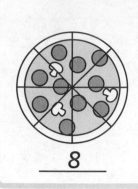  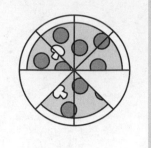

8 _____   7 _____   _____

apples on a plate

_____   _____   _____

dots in a row

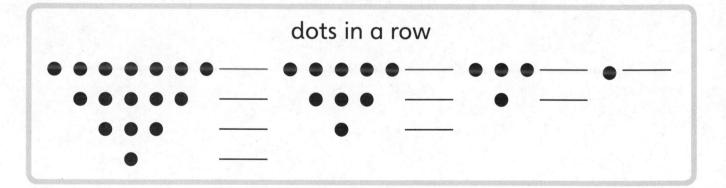

_____   _____   _____

children in a line

  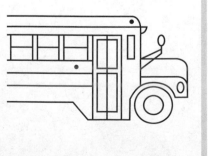

_____   _____   _____

Patterns and Algebra 2-8

<table>
<tr>
<td>
8   5</td>
<td>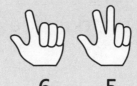
8   7   6   5</td>
<td>8 − 3 = 5
5 is 3 less than 8.</td>
</tr>
</table>

☐ Write the number you subtract in the circles.

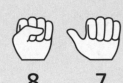
6   5

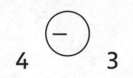
4   3

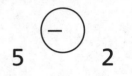
5   2

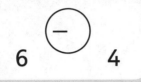
6   4

7   6

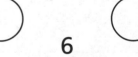
8   4

12   10

12   11

16   14

19   15

18   12

17   10

7   6   5

10   9   8

6   4   2

13   12   11

8   6   4

 says the next number is 2. How does he know?

_____

Describing Patterns

☐ Write the number you add in the circles.
☐ Describe the pattern.

1 (+2) 3 (+2) 5
Start at __1__.
Add __2__ each time.

4 (+) 6 (+) 8
Start at _____.
Add _____ each time.

5 (+) 6 (+) 7
Start at _____.
Add _____ each time.

10 (+) 15 (+) 20
Start at _____.
Add _____ each time.

10 ◯ 20 ◯ 30 ◯ 40 ◯ 50 ◯ 60
Start at _____. Add _____.

7 ◯ 10 ◯ 13 ◯ 16 ◯ 19 ◯ 22
Start at _____. _____.

0 ◯ 5 ◯ 10 ◯ 15 ◯ 20 ◯ 25
_____. _____.

Patterns and Algebra 2-9

☐ Write the number you subtract in the circles.
☐ Describe the pattern.

7 (−2) 5 (−2) 3
Start at ___7___.
Subtract ___2___ each time.

8 (−) 7 (−) 6
Start at _____.
Subtract _____ each time.

10 (−) 8 (−) 6
Start at _____.
Subtract _____ each time.

30 (−) 20 (−) 10
Start at _____.
Subtract _____ each time.

12 ( ) 10 ( ) 8 ( ) 6 ( ) 4 ( ) 2
Start at _____. Subtract _____.

18 ( ) 15 ( ) 12 ( ) 9 ( ) 6 ( ) 3
Start at _____. _____.

35 ( ) 30 ( ) 25 ( ) 20 ( ) 15 ( ) 10
_____. _____.

☐ Write the number you add or subtract in the circles.
☐ Describe the pattern.

7 (−1) 6 (−1) 5
Start at __7__.
Subtract __1__ each time.

7 (−) 5 (−) 3
Start at _____.
Subtract _____ each time.

15 (+) 16 (+) 17 (+) 18 (+) 19
Start at _____. Add _____ each time.

1 (+) 3 (+) 5 (+) 7 (+) 9
Start at _____. Add _____ each time.

8 (−) 7 (−) 6 (−) 5 (−) 4
Start at _____. Subtract _____.

8 (+) 9 (+) 10 (+) 11 (+) 12
Start at _____. Add _____.

8 (−) 6 (−) 4 (−) 2 (−) 0
Start at _____. Subtract _____.

☐ Make the pattern for the rule.

Start at 1. Add 2 each time.

$\underline{\quad 1 \quad}$ (+2) $\underline{\quad 3 \quad}$ (+2) $\underline{\quad 5 \quad}$ (+2) $\underline{\quad 7 \quad}$ (+2) $\underline{\quad 9 \quad}$

Start at 5. Add 1 each time.

$\underline{\quad 5 \quad}$ (+1) $\underline{\quad 6 \quad}$ (+1) $\underline{\qquad}$ (+1) $\underline{\qquad}$ (+1) $\underline{\qquad}$

Start at 10. Subtract 2 each time.

$\underline{\quad 10 \quad}$ (−2) $\underline{\qquad}$ (−2) $\underline{\qquad}$ ◯ $\underline{\qquad}$ ◯ $\underline{\qquad}$

Start at 3. Add 10 each time.

◯ $\underline{\qquad}$ ◯ $\underline{\qquad}$ ◯ $\underline{\qquad}$ ◯ $\underline{\qquad}$

Start at 16. Subtract 2 each time.

◯ $\underline{\qquad}$ ◯ $\underline{\qquad}$ ◯ $\underline{\qquad}$ ◯ $\underline{\qquad}$

☐ Make your own rule and make the pattern.

Start at _____. _____.

◯ $\underline{\qquad}$ ◯ $\underline{\qquad}$ ◯ $\underline{\qquad}$ ◯ $\underline{\qquad}$

Identifying Patterns

☐ Write **R** if the pattern **R**epeats.
☐ Write **G** if the pattern **G**rows.
☐ Write **S** if the pattern **S**hrinks.

4 5 6 7 8 9 10 11	_G_
4 3 2 4 3 2 4 3 2	___
10 9 8 7 6 5 4 3 2	___
3 5 7 9 11 13 15 17	___
3 5 7 3 5 7 3 5 7 3 5 7	___
100 90 80 70 60 50 40	___
5 10 15 20 25 30 35	___

Patterns and Algebra 2-10

☐ Add or subtract.
☐ Does each pattern repeat, grow, or shrink?
   Write **R**, **G**, or **S** beside each pattern.

3	3	3	3	3	3	3	
+ 1	+ 2	+ 3	+ 4	+ 5	+ 6	+ 7	_R_
4	5	6	7	8	9	10	_G_
							_G_

9	8	7	6	5	4	3	
+ 2	+ 2	+ 2	+ 2	+ 2	+ 2	+ 2	_____
							_____
							_____

9	8	7	6	5	4	3	2	
+ 1	+ 2	+ 3	+ 4	+ 5	+ 6	+ 7	+ 8	_____
								_____
								_____

3	5	7	9	11	13	15	
− 2	− 2	− 2	− 2	− 2	− 2	− 2	_____
							_____
							_____

12	11	10	9	8	7	6	
− 0	− 1	− 2	− 3	− 4	− 5	− 6	_____
							_____

☐ Describe the pattern.

1   3   5   7   9

Start at ___*1*___.

Add ___*2*___ each time.

___*large, small, small,*___

___*then repeat*___

---

8   7   6   5   4

Start at _____.

Subtract _____.

30   40   50   60   70

Start at _____.

Add _____.

---

12   10   8   6   4

_____

_____

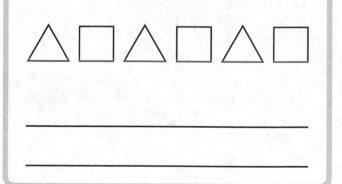

_____

_____

---

5   10   15   20   25

_____

_____

100   98   96   94

_____

_____

Patterns in a Hundreds Chart

1	2	3	4	5	6	7	8	9	10
11	(12)	13	14	15	16	17	18	19	20
21	22	(23)	24	25	26	27	28	29	30
31	32	33	(34)	35	36	37	38	39	40
41	42	43	44	(45)	46	47	48	49	50
51	52	53	54	55	(56)	57	58	59	60

☐ Describe the pattern in the **ones digits**.

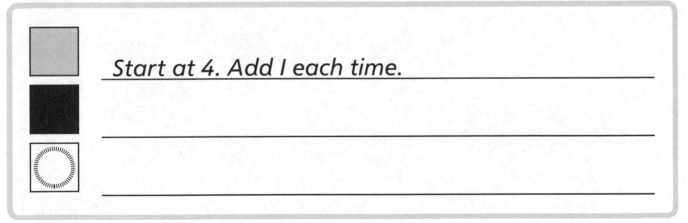

◻ (grey)
◼ (black)
⃝ (circle)

Start at 4. Add 1 each time.

_____

_____

☐ Describe the pattern in the **tens digits**.

◻ (grey) _____

◼ (black) _____

⃝ (circle) _____

11	(12)	13	14	15	16	17	18	19	20
21	22	(23)	24	25	26	27	28	29	30
31	32	33	(34)	35	36	37	38	39	40
41	42	43	44	(45)	46	47	48	49	50
51	52	53	54	55	(56)	57	58	59	60

☐ Circle the correct word.
☐ Copy the pattern.
☐ Write the number you add in the circles.
☐ Describe the pattern.

■ are all in the same column / diagonal / (row.)

__24__ (+1) __25__ (+1) __26__ (+1) __27__ (+1) __28__ (+1) __29__

Start at 24. Add 1 each time.

■ are all in the same column / diagonal / row.

__11__ ◯ __21__ ◯ ____ ◯ ____ ◯ ____

Start at _____.

▣ are all in the same column / diagonal / row.

____ ◯ ____ ◯ ____ ◯ ____ ◯ ____

_____

Patterns and Algebra 2-11

Finding Mistakes

☐ Write the number you add in the circles.
☐ Write the missing number.

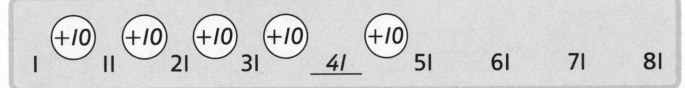

1 (+10) 11 (+10) 21 (+10) 31 (+10) ___41___ (+10) 51   61   71   81

10 (+3) 13 ◯ 16 ◯ ___ ◯ 22   25   28   31

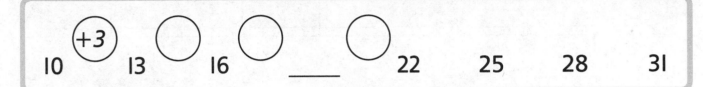

10 ◯ 12 ◯ 14 ◯ ___ ◯ 18   20   22   24

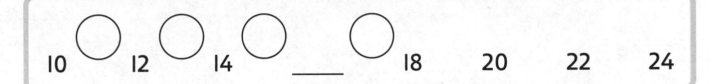

15 ◯ 20 ◯ 25 ◯ 30 ◯ ___ ◯ 40   45   50

☐ Now draw the circles and write the numbers.

4   14   24   ___   44   54   64   74

5   7   9   11   ___   15   17   19

Bonus

1   4   7   ___   13   16   19   22   25

What is the missing room number?

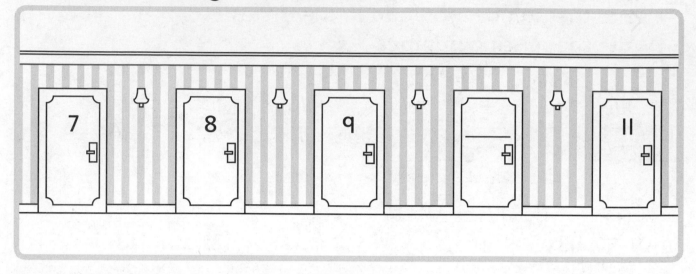

What is the missing house number?

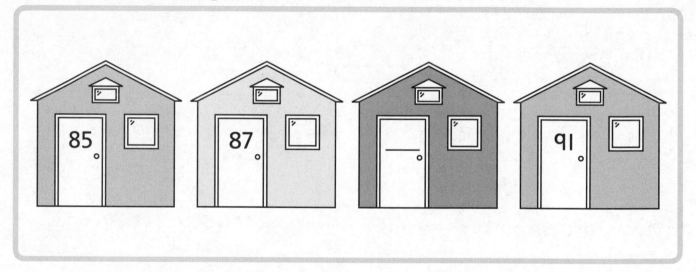

☐ Find the missing page number.

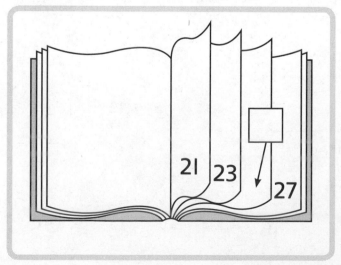

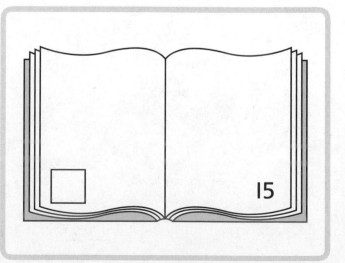

☐ Write the numbers you add in the circles.
☐ ✗ the number that does not fit.
☐ Find the missing number.

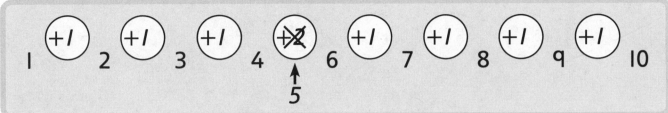

1 (+1) 2 (+1) 3 (+1) 4 (+✗2) 6 (+1) 7 (+1) 8 (+1) 9 (+1) 10
↑
5

0 ◯ 2 ◯ 4 ◯ 6 ◯ 8 ◯ 10 ◯ 14 ◯ 16

0 ◯ 3 ◯ 6 ◯ 9 ◯ 12 ◯ 18 ◯ 21 ◯ 24 ◯ 27

3 ◯ 7 ◯ 9 ◯ 11 ◯ 13 ◯ 15 ◯ 17 ◯ 19

15 ◯ 20 ◯ 25 ◯ 35 ◯ 40 ◯ 45 ◯ 50

Bonus

4 ◯ 8 ◯ 12 ◯ 16 ◯ 24 ◯ 28 ◯ 32 ◯ 36

☐ Write the numbers you add in the circles.
☐ ✗ the mistakes in the pattern.
☐ Correct the mistakes.

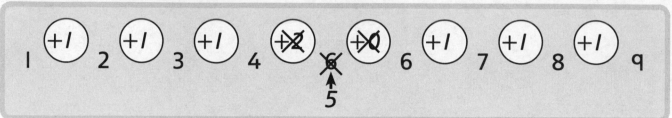

1 (+1) 2 (+1) 3 (+1) 4 (+✗2) ✗6 (+✗0) 6 (+1) 7 (+1) 8 (+1) 9
                                  ↑
                                  5

2 (+2) 4 (+2) 6 (+2) 8 (+1) 9 (+3) 12 (+2) 14

5 ◯ 10 ◯ 15 ◯ 22 ◯ 25 ◯ 30

2 ◯ 7 ◯ 12 ◯ 17 ◯ 22 ◯ 28 ◯ 32

0 ◯ 20 ◯ 40 ◯ 70 ◯ 80 ◯ 100

Bonus

10 ◯ 20 ◯ 30 ◯ 40 ◯ 5 ◯ 60

Patterns and Algebra 2-12

Showing Patterns in Different Ways

☐ Write numbers to show the pattern.

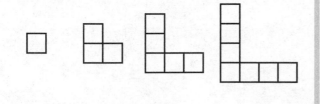

Aa   Aaa   Aaaa

_2_   _3_   _4_

___   ___   ___

___ ___ ___ ___

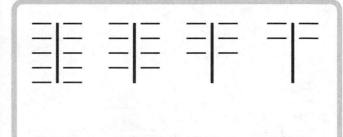

___ ___ ___ ___

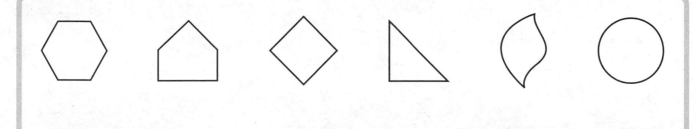

___ ___ ___

___ ___ ___ ___

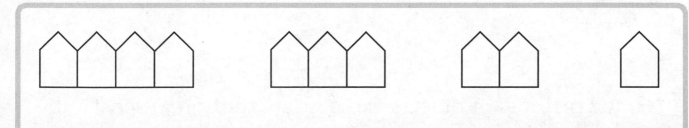

___ ___ ___ ___ ___ ___

___ ___ ___ ___

Cubes

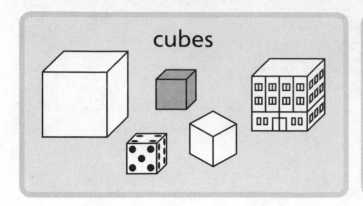

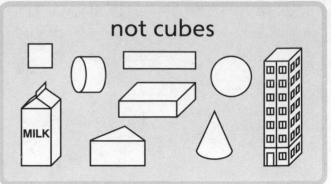

☐ Circle the cubes.

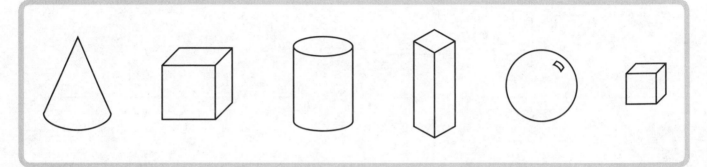

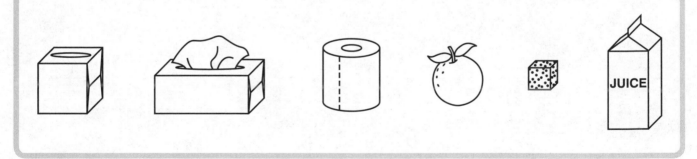

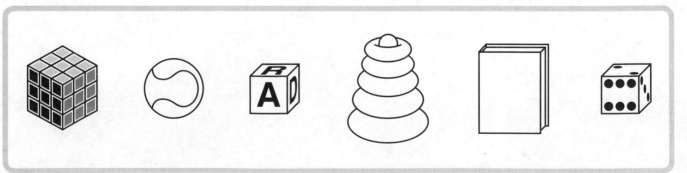

 Find 2 pictures of objects like a that are almost cubes. Glue them into your 📓.

Spheres and Cylinders

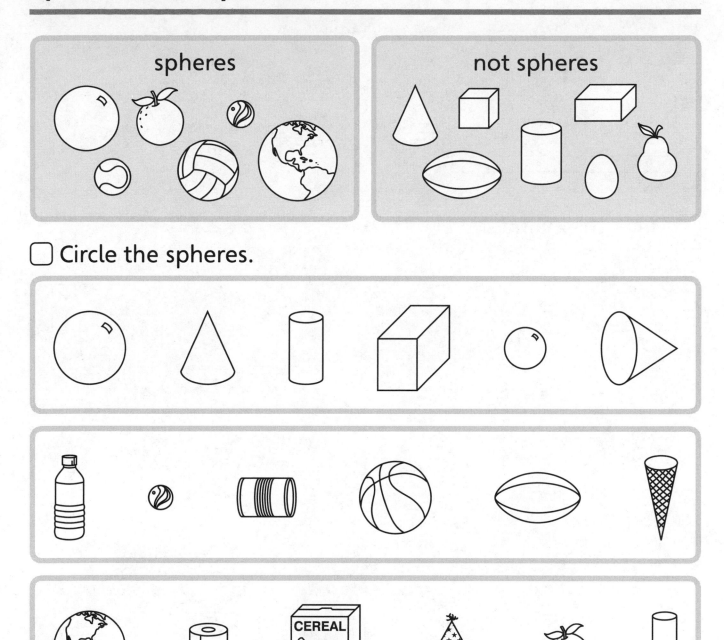

spheres

not spheres

☐ Circle the spheres.

☐ Draw 2 more objects that are almost spheres.

cylinders	not cylinders
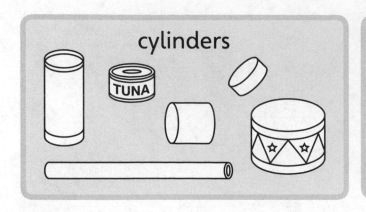	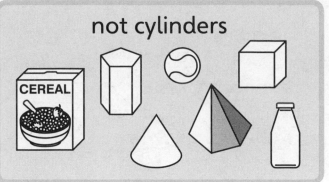

☐ Circle the cylinders.

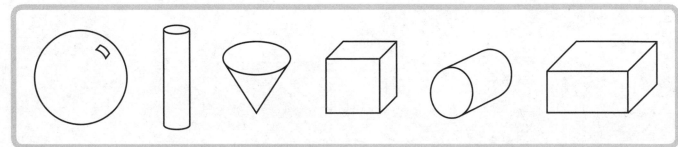

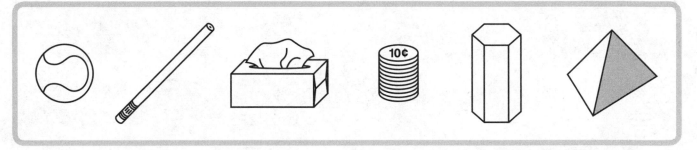

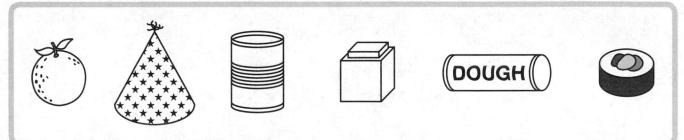

☐ Draw 2 more objects that are almost cylinders.

Geometry 2-15

Cones

cones

not cones

☐ Circle the cones.

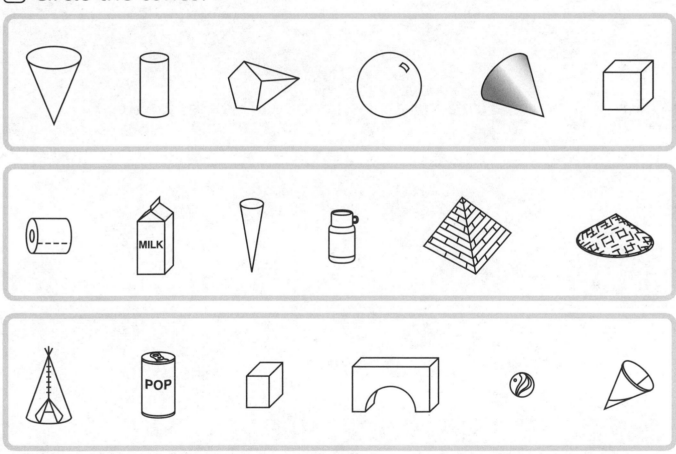

☐ Draw 2 more objects that are almost cones.

☐ Match the pictures to the kind of shape.

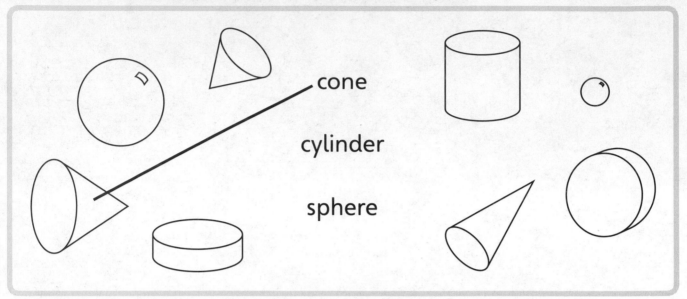

cone

cylinder

sphere

☐ Are they the same kind of shape? Write **yes** or **no**.

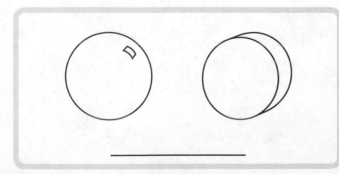

_____no_____

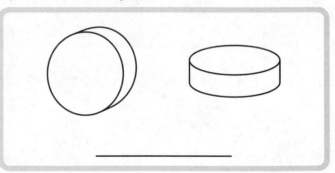

_____

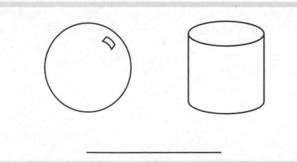

_____

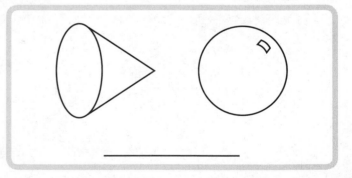

_____

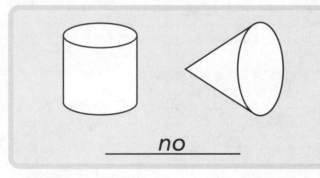

_____

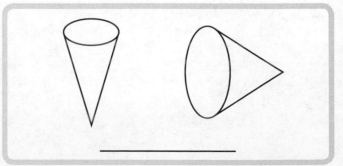

_____

Pyramids

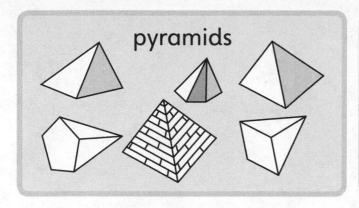
pyramids

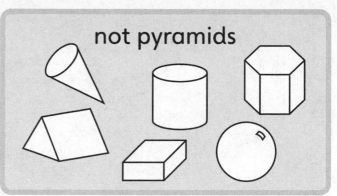
not pyramids

☐ Circle the pyramids.

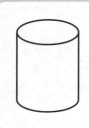 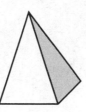  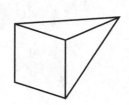

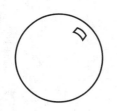 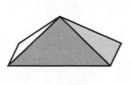 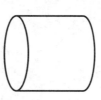 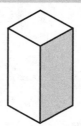 

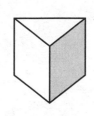  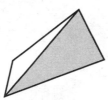  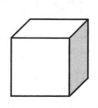

☐ Colour the pyramids in the pictures.

 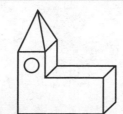 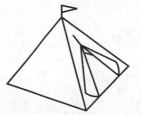 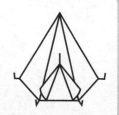

Prisms

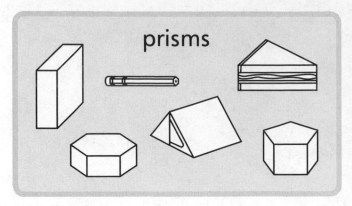
prisms

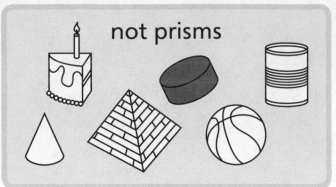
not prisms

☐ Circle the prisms.

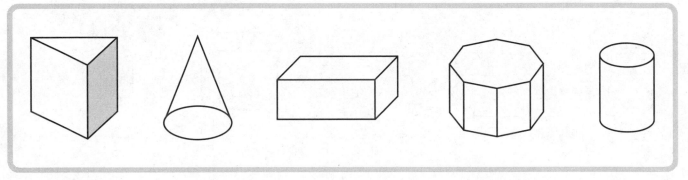

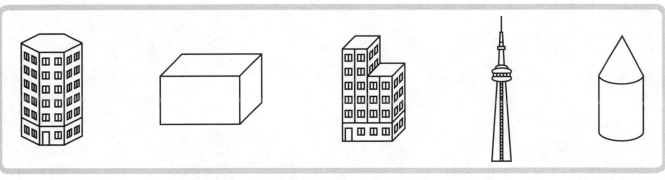

📓 Find 2 pictures of objects like a that are almost prisms.
Glue them into your 📓.

Turning 3-D Shapes

Was the shape **changed** or **turned**?

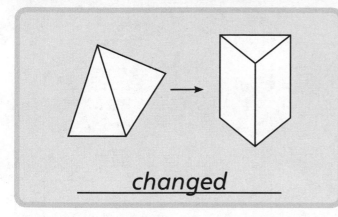

changed

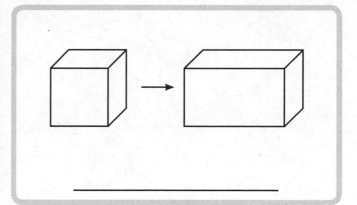

_____

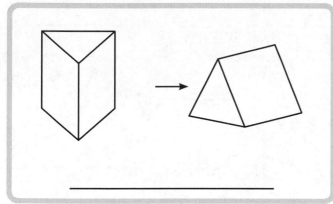

_____

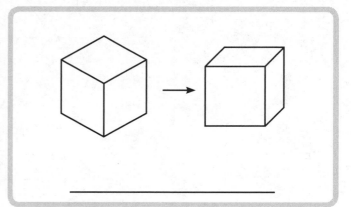

_____

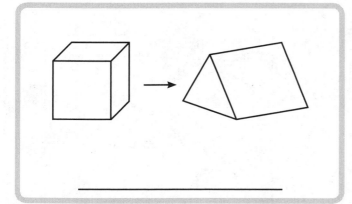

_____

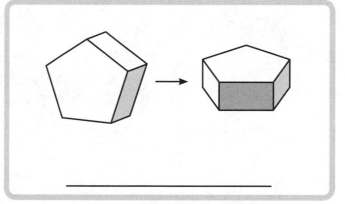

_____

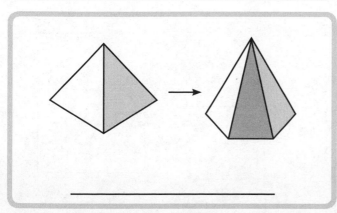

_____

Bonus

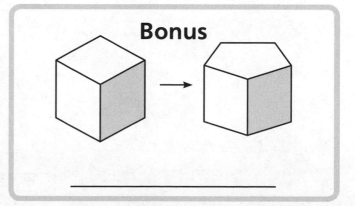

_____

Faces

☐ What is the shape of the shaded face? Circle it.

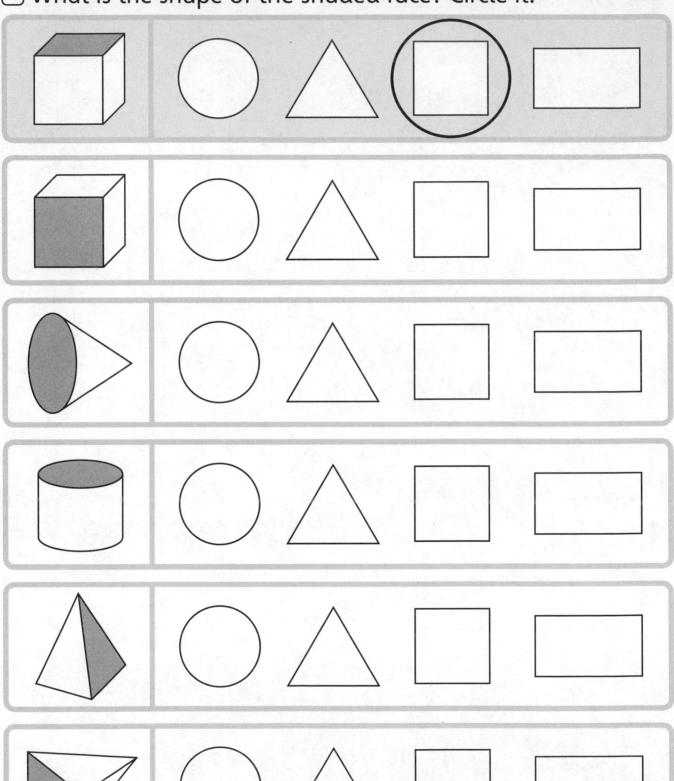

☐ What is the shape of the shaded face? ✗ it.

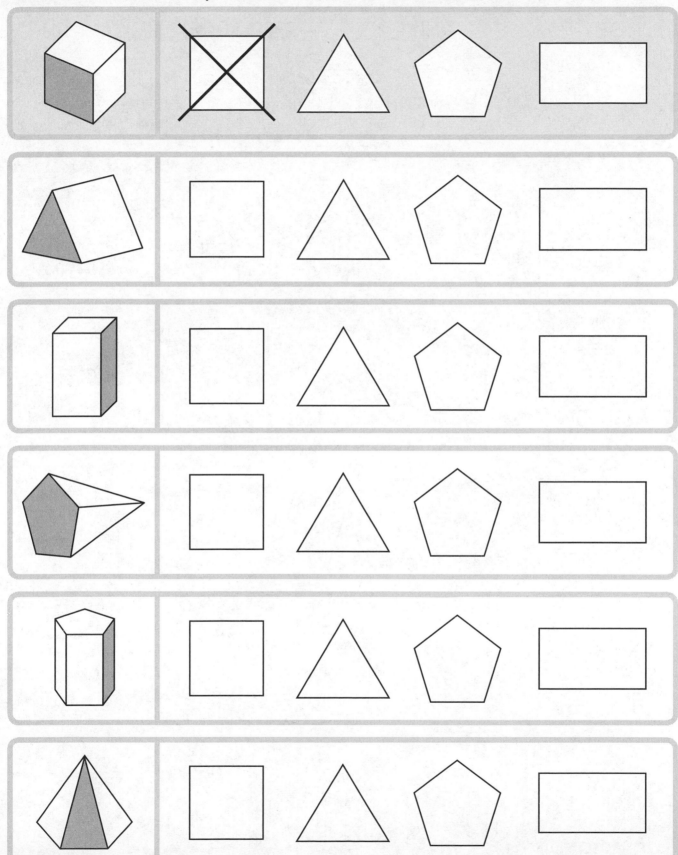

Use real 3-D shapes.

☐ Circle the shapes with a face that matches the given shape.

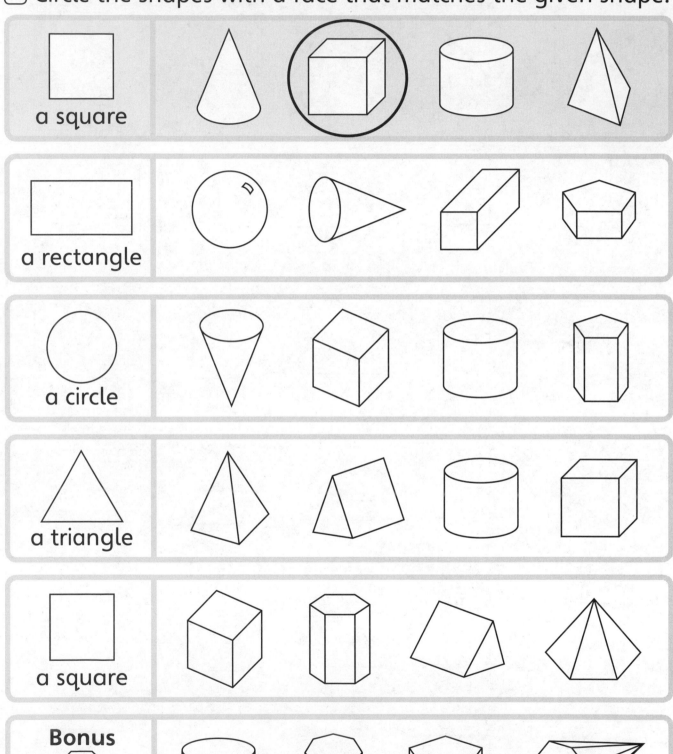

98

Shapes in Structures

☐ ✓ the shapes you see in the structure.

☐ pyramid
☑ cube
☐ cone
☑ cylinder
☐ sphere

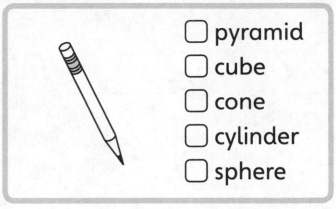
☐ pyramid
☐ cube
☐ cone
☐ cylinder
☐ sphere

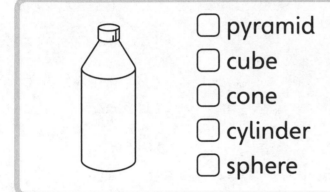
☐ pyramid
☐ cube
☐ cone
☐ cylinder
☐ sphere

☐ pyramid
☐ cube
☐ cone
☐ cylinder
☐ sphere

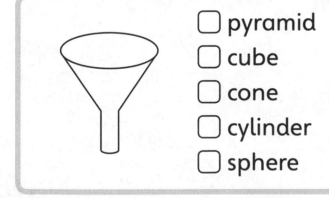
☐ pyramid
☐ cube
☐ cone
☐ cylinder
☐ sphere

☐ pyramid
☐ cube
☐ cone
☐ cylinder
☐ sphere

☐ pyramid
☐ cube
☐ cone
☐ cylinder
☐ sphere

☐ pyramid
☐ cube
☐ cone
☐ cylinder
☐ sphere

☐ Count the 3-D shapes that you see.

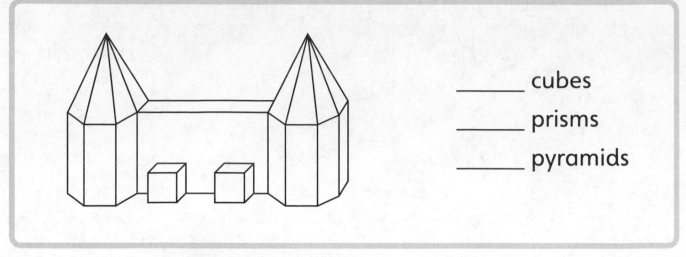

_____ cubes

_____ prisms

_____ pyramids

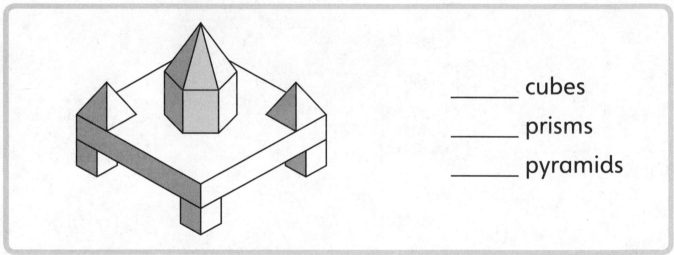

_____ cubes

_____ prisms

_____ pyramids

Bonus

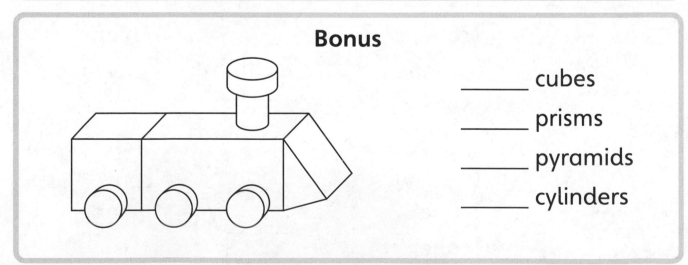

_____ cubes

_____ prisms

_____ pyramids

_____ cylinders

📓 Build your own structure from blocks.
How many of each shape did you use?

How are the shapes sorted?

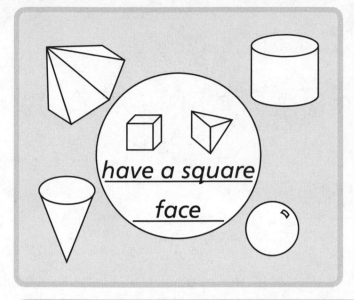

have a square

face

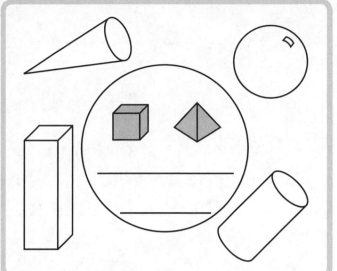

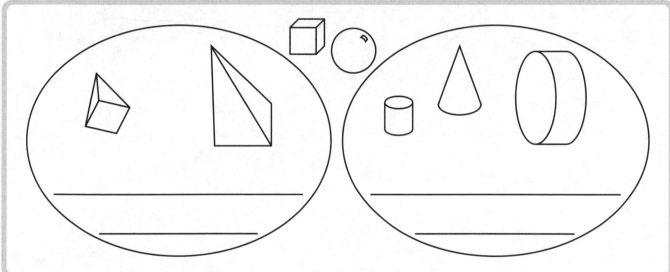

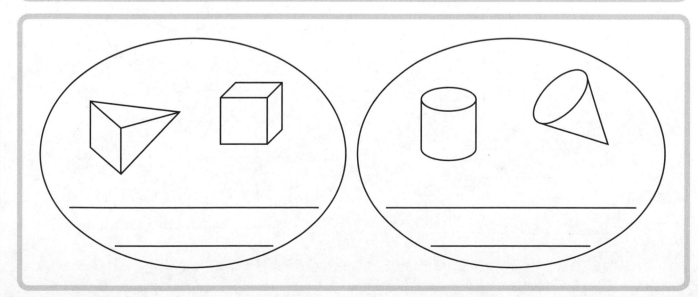

Roll, Slide, Stack

Curved faces roll. 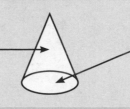 **Flat** faces slide.

☐ ✓ what the shape can do.
☐ Colour the **curved** faces orange.
☐ Colour the **flat** faces blue.

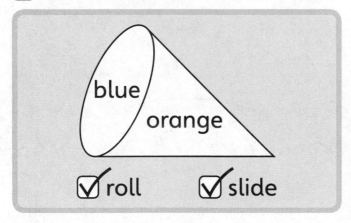

blue
orange

☑ roll   ☑ slide

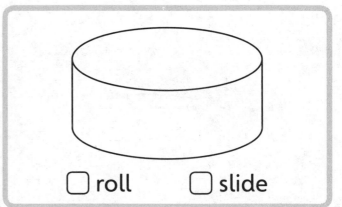

☐ roll   ☐ slide

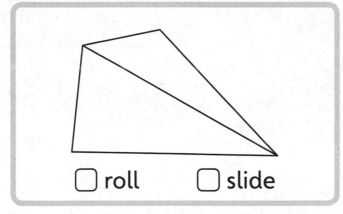

☐ roll   ☐ slide

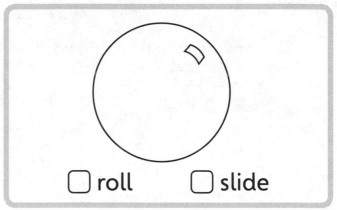

☐ roll   ☐ slide

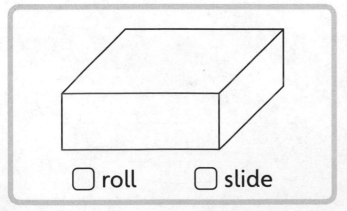

☐ roll   ☐ slide

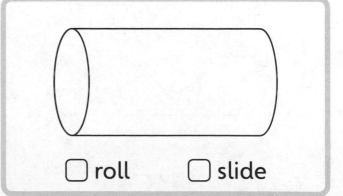

☐ roll   ☐ slide

☐ Use the letters to sort the shapes.

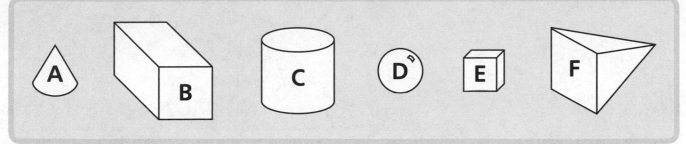

large	small
B	A

has a ☐ face	has a ○ face

has a curved face	has only flat faces
A	B

only rolls	rolls and slides	only slides

📓 Choose another geometric attribute and sort the shapes again.

Vertices

vertices	not vertices
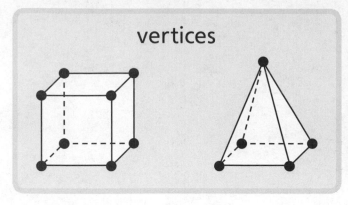	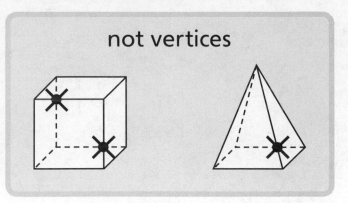

☐ Draw a ● on each vertex.
☐ Count the vertices.

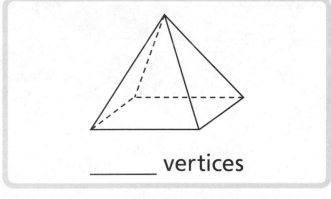

_____4_____ vertices

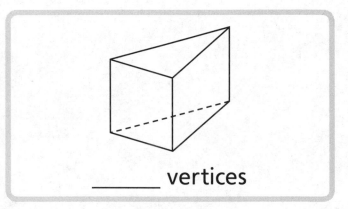

_____ vertices

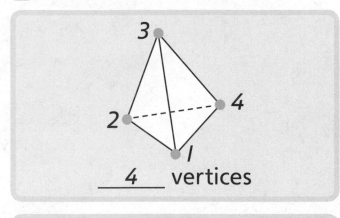

_____ vertices

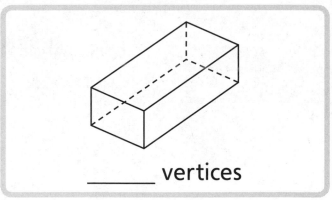

_____ vertices

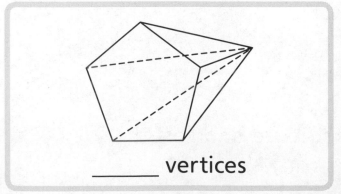

_____ vertices

Bonus

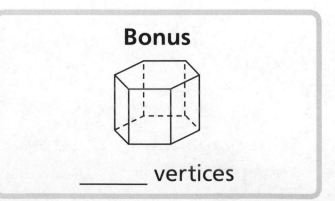

_____ vertices

Edges

This shape has **6 edges**.

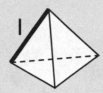 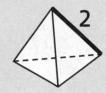 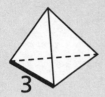  

☐ Count the edges.

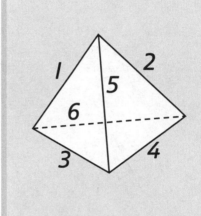

_____6_____ edges

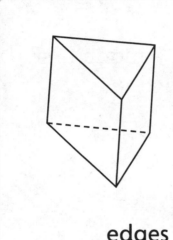

_____ edges

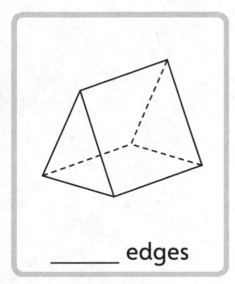

_____ edges

_____ edges

_____ edges

Bonus

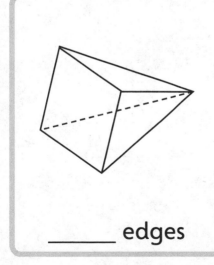

_____ edges

▤ Use a real 3-D object.
How many faces meet at each edge?
Compare your answer with a partner.

☐ Make skeletons of pyramids from straws 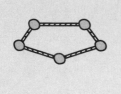 and clay 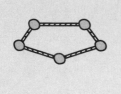. Follow these steps.

1. Make a polygon.	2. Put a ▱ in each ◐.	3. Join the ▱ to another ◐.

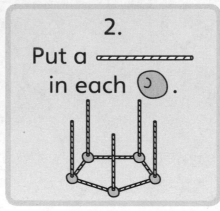

☐ Colour the polygon you made **first**.
☐ Circle the ◐ you added **last**.

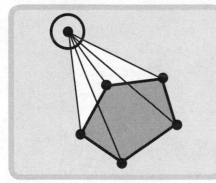
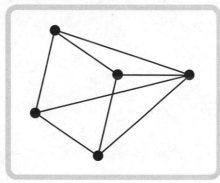
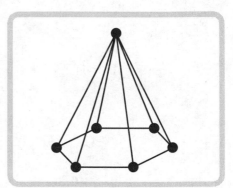

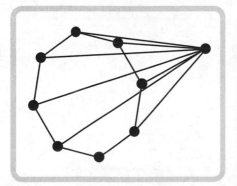
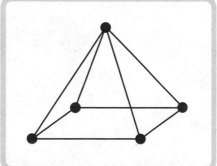
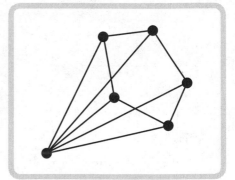

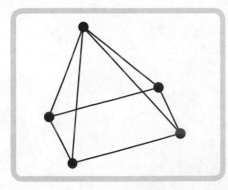
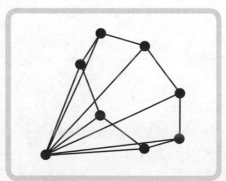
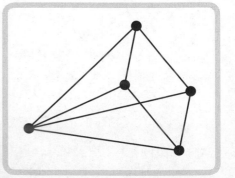

Geometry 2-24

Left, Right, Above, Below

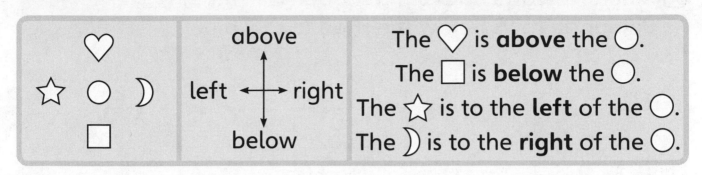

The ♡ is **above** the ◯.
The ☐ is **below** the ◯.
The ☆ is to the **left** of the ◯.
The ☽ is to the **right** of the ◯.

☐ Circle the shape on the **left**.

☐ Circle the shape on the **right**.

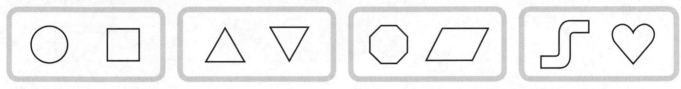

Where is the circle?

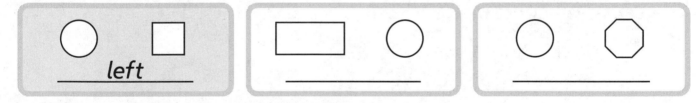

left

☐ Circle the shape that is **above** the other.

☐ Circle the shape that is **below** the other.

☐ Colour all rows **above** the shaded row red.
☐ Colour all rows **below** the shaded row blue.

☐ Colour all columns to the **left** of the shaded column green.
☐ Colour all columns to the **right** of the shaded column yellow.

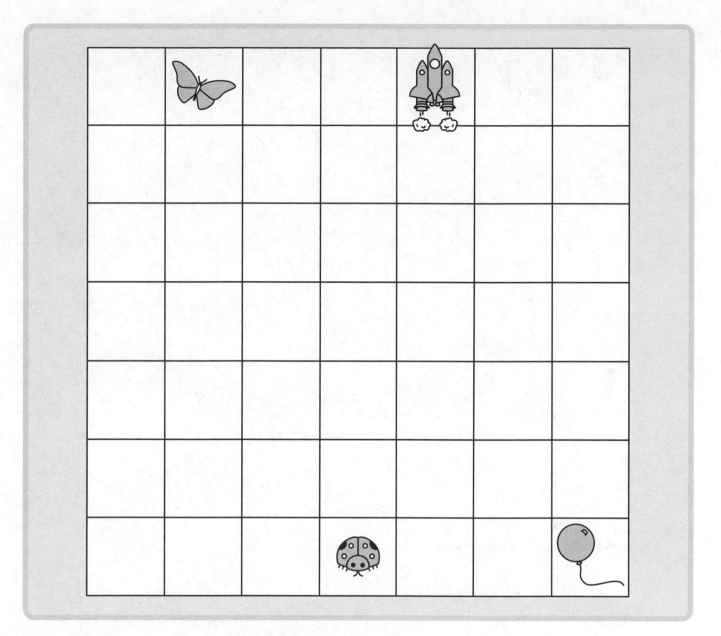

☐ Colour the first 5 squares above the ladybug green.
☐ Colour the first 5 squares below the butterfly green.
☐ Draw a dot in the square to the right of the rocket.
 Colour the square below the dot yellow.
☐ Draw a dot in the square to the left of the balloon.
 Colour the first 3 squares above the dot yellow.
☐ Find the square between the two green columns that is
 directly in the middle and colour it green.
☐ What word do you see? _____

Maps

teacher's desk	whiteboard	shelf	
	students' desks	reading corner / shelf	in front of
			left ← → right
round table	carpet	math centre	behind
		door	

in front of	~~left of~~	right of	behind

☐ Fill in the blanks.

Where is the teacher's desk? To the _____*left of*_____ the students' desks.

Where is the reading corner? _____ the math centre.

Where is the math centre? To the _____ the carpet.

Where is the carpet? _____ the students' desks.

📓 Write 2 questions about this map.
Ask a friend to answer them.

📓 Draw a map of your classroom. Show where you sit. Write 4 sentences telling where some classroom objects are.

Eddy's room

Each square is 1 step long.

- How many steps are between the closet and the bed?
  _____ steps.

- Fill in the blanks.

  The closet is ___2___ steps to the ___right___ of the desk.

  The bed is _____ steps to the ___left___ of the desk.

  The wide shelf is _____ steps to the _____ of
  the door.

- Eddy stands in front of the door. He goes 2 steps forward.
  Draw a dot where Eddy stops.

- Eddy starts at the dot. He goes 4 steps left and 2 steps
  forward to get to the beanbag chair. Draw the
  beanbag chair.

- How do you get from the door to the bed?

Three-Digit Numbers

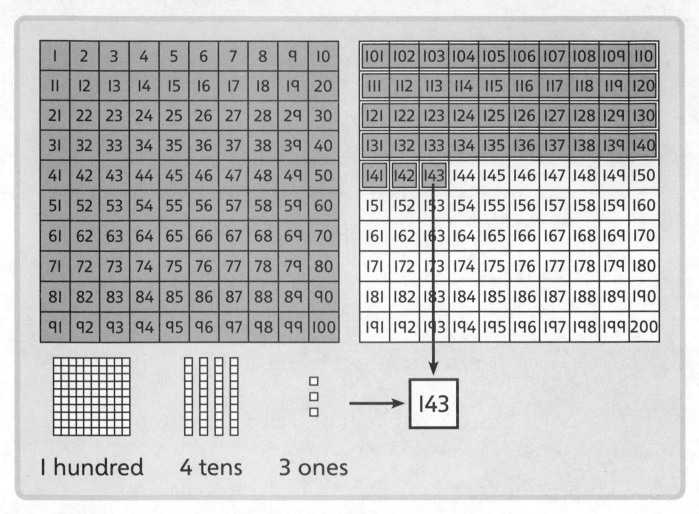

I hundred   4 tens   3 ones

What number does the set show?

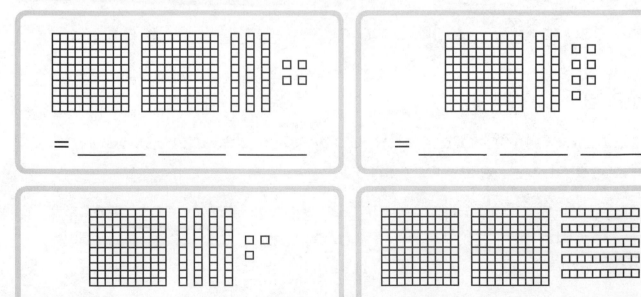

= _____ _____ _____

= _____ _____ _____

= _____ _____ _____

= _____ _____ _____

How many dots?

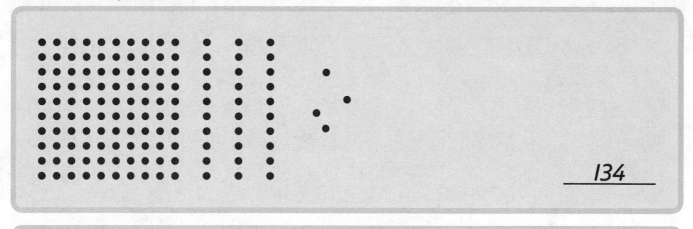

_134_

_____

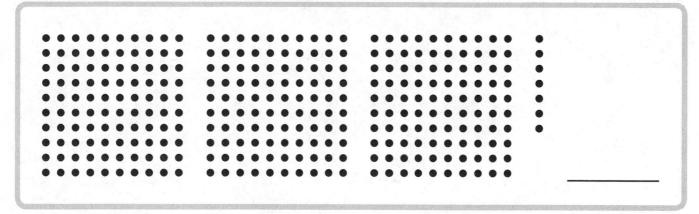

_____

_____

A **ones** digit of 4 means $4 = 1 + 1 + 1 + 1$

A **tens** digit of 5 means $50 = 10 + 10 + 10 + 10 + 10$

A **hundreds** digit of 3 means $300 = 100 + 100 + 100$

☐ Write the number as a sum of 100s, 10s, and 1s.

$324 = 100 + 100 + 100 + 10 + 10 + 1 + 1 + 1 + 1$

$213 =$

$320 =$

☐ We can write $324 = 300 + 20 + 4$. Write the number in this way.

$102 = 100 + 2$	$546 =$
$904 =$	$490 =$

☐ Add.

$400 + 70 = \underline{}$	$400 + 7 = \underline{}$	$300 + 50 = \underline{}$
$200 + 70 = \underline{}$	$60 + 100 = \underline{}$	$9 + 300 = \underline{}$

$30 + 2 + 400 = \underline{}$ $20 + 500 + 4 = \underline{}$

Bonus: $2000 + 300 + 7 = \underline{}$

Skip Counting to Large Numbers

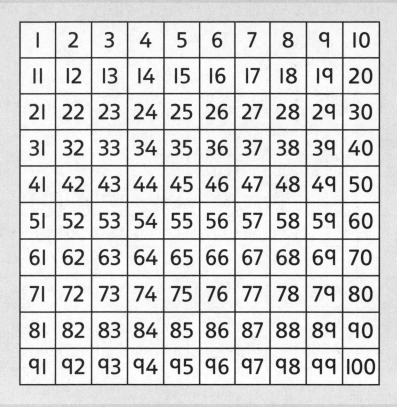

☐ Count by 5s.

70 ____ ____ ____ ____ ____

☐ Count by 10s.

35 ____ ____ ____ ____ ____

☐ Count by 25s.

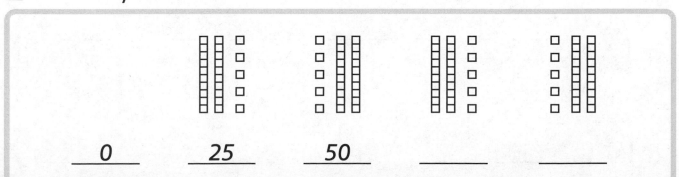

__0__   __25__   __50__   ____   ____

Start at **5**.

Shade the numbers you say when skip counting by 5s.

1	2	3	4	5	6	7	8	9	10
11	12	13	14	15	16	17	18	19	20
21	22	23	24	25	26	27	28	29	30
31	32	33	34	35	36	37	38	39	40
41	42	43	44	45	46	47	48	49	50
51	52	53	54	55	56	57	58	59	60
61	62	63	64	65	66	67	68	69	70
71	72	73	74	75	76	77	78	79	80
81	82	83	84	85	86	87	88	89	90
91	92	93	94	95	96	97	98	99	100

101	102	103	104	105	106	107	108	109	110
111	112	113	114	115	116	117	118	119	120
121	122	123	124	125	126	127	128	129	130
131	132	133	134	135	136	137	138	139	140
141	142	143	144	145	146	147	148	149	150
151	152	153	154	155	156	157	158	159	160
161	162	163	164	165	166	167	168	169	170
171	172	173	174	175	176	177	178	179	180
181	182	183	184	185	186	187	188	189	190
191	192	193	194	195	196	197	198	199	200

Count by 5s.

85 _____ _____ _____ _____ *110* _____

140 _____ _____ _____ _____ _____ _____

Count by 10s.

70 _____ _____ _____ _____ _____ _____ _____

Count by 2s.

142 _____ _____ _____ _____ _____ _____ _____

☐ Shade the numbers you say when skip counting by 25s.

1	2	3	4	5	6	7	8	9	10
11	12	13	14	15	16	17	18	19	20
21	22	23	24	25	26	27	28	29	30
31	32	33	34	35	36	37	38	39	40
41	42	43	44	45	46	47	48	49	50
51	52	53	54	55	56	57	58	59	60
61	62	63	64	65	66	67	68	69	70
71	72	73	74	75	76	77	78	79	80
81	82	83	84	85	86	87	88	89	90
91	92	93	94	95	96	97	98	99	100

101	102	103	104	105	106	107	108	109	110
111	112	113	114	115	116	117	118	119	120
121	122	123	124	125	126	127	128	129	130
131	132	133	134	135	136	137	138	139	140
141	142	143	144	145	146	147	148	149	150
151	152	153	154	155	156	157	158	159	160
161	162	163	164	165	166	167	168	169	170
171	172	173	174	175	176	177	178	179	180
181	182	183	184	185	186	187	188	189	190
191	192	193	194	195	196	197	198	199	200

☐ Count by 25s from 0 to 200.

_0_   _25_   ____   ____   ____

_125_   ____   ____   ____

☐ Count by 25s.

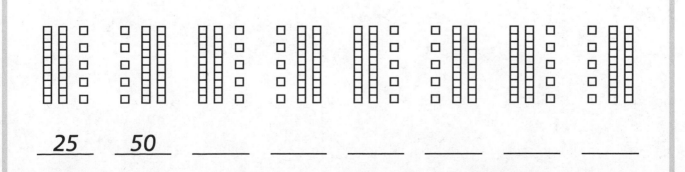

_25_   _50_   ____   ____   ____   ____   ____   ____

Skip Counting by Different Numbers

☐ Count by , then by .

    16   17   18

 5

☐ Count by 10s, then by .

10   20   30   40   50   51   52

 10

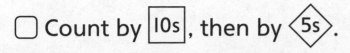 Count by ☐ 10s , then by ◇ 5s .

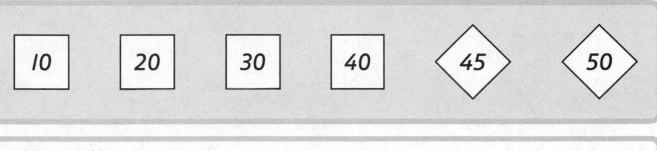

| 10 | 20 | 30 | 40 | 45 | 50 |

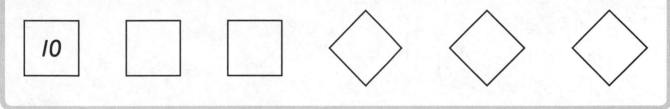

| 10 | | | | | |

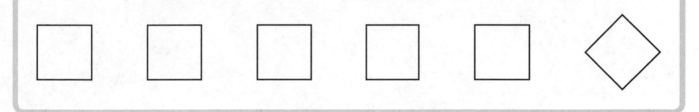

☐ Count by 10s , then by 5s , then by 1s .

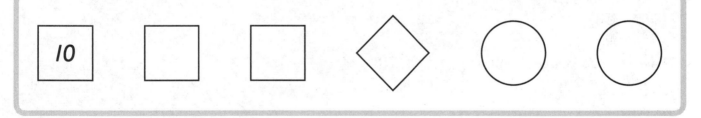

| 10 | | | | | |

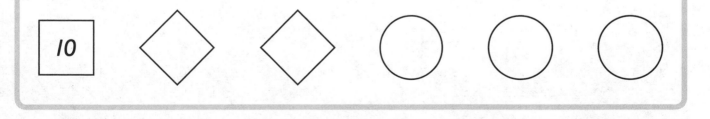

| 10 | | | | | |

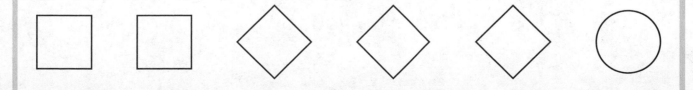

☐ Count by ⟨25s⟩, ⟨10s⟩, ⟨5s⟩, and ⟨1s⟩.

| 〰25〰 | 〰50〰 | 60 | 70 | 80 | 81 | 82 |

| 〰25〰 | 35 | | | ◇ | ◇ | ◯ |

| 〰〰 | 〰〰 | 〰〰 | ☐ | ◇ | ◇ | ◯ |

| 〰〰 | 〰〰 | ☐ | ◇ | ◇ | ◇ | ◯ |

| 〰〰 | 〰〰 | ☐ | ☐ | ◇ | ◯ | ◯ |

| 〰〰 | ☐ | ☐ | ◇ | ◯ | ◯ | ◯ |

Make up your own.

Coin Values

☐ Write the **value** on the coin.
☐ Write the **name** of the coin.

quarter	loonie	dime
nickel	~~penny~~	toonie

_____penny_____

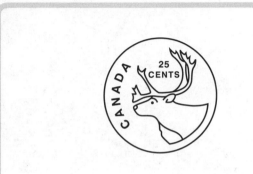

_____

_____

_____

_____

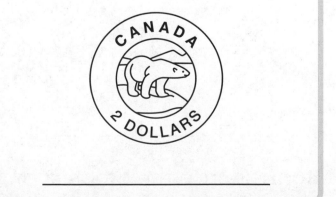

_____

Counting Coins

☐ Skip count by the coin value.

5¢	5¢	5¢	5¢	5¢	5¢	5¢

__5__ ¢   __10__ ¢   _____ ¢   _____ ¢   _____ ¢   _____ ¢   _____ ¢

10¢	10¢	10¢	10¢	10¢	10¢	10¢

_____ ¢   _____ ¢   _____ ¢   _____ ¢   _____ ¢   _____ ¢   _____ ¢

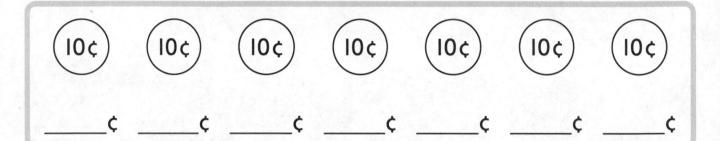

_____ ¢   _____ ¢   _____ ¢   _____ ¢   _____ ¢   _____ ¢   _____ ¢

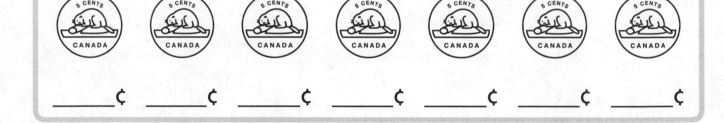

_____ ¢   _____ ¢   _____ ¢   _____ ¢   _____ ¢   _____ ¢   _____ ¢

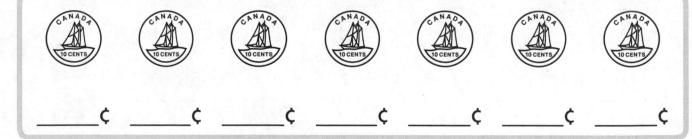

_____ ¢   _____ ¢   _____ ¢   _____ ¢

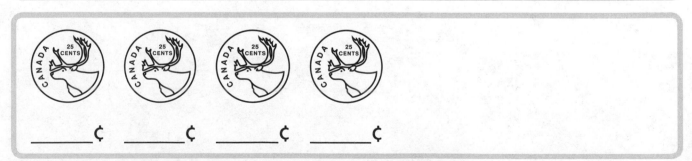

Bonus: Circle the greatest amount of money.

☐ Count the money by the coin value.

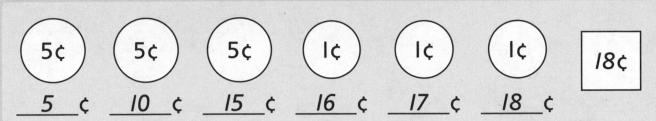

5¢	5¢	5¢	1¢	1¢	1¢	18¢

__5__ ¢   __10__ ¢   __15__ ¢   __16__ ¢   __17__ ¢   __18__ ¢

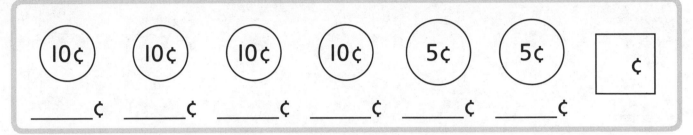

10¢	10¢	10¢	10¢	5¢	5¢	¢

____ ¢   ____ ¢   ____ ¢   ____ ¢   ____ ¢   ____ ¢

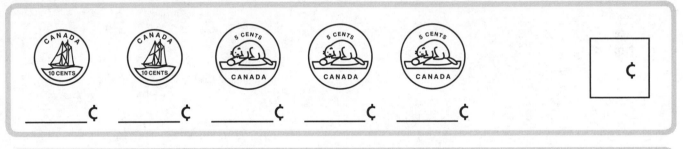

____ ¢   ____ ¢   ____ ¢   ____ ¢   ____ ¢

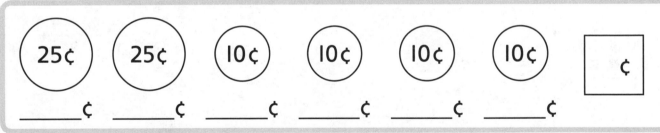

25¢	25¢	10¢	10¢	10¢	10¢	¢

____ ¢   ____ ¢   ____ ¢   ____ ¢   ____ ¢   ____ ¢

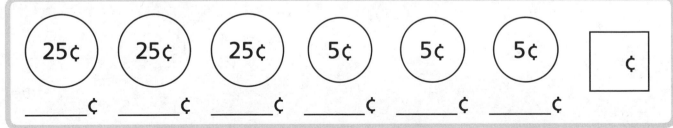

25¢	25¢	25¢	5¢	5¢	5¢	¢

____ ¢   ____ ¢   ____ ¢   ____ ¢   ____ ¢   ____ ¢

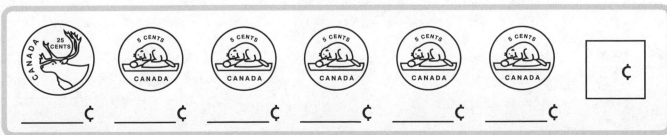

____ ¢   ____ ¢   ____ ¢   ____ ¢   ____ ¢   ____ ¢

☐ Count the money.

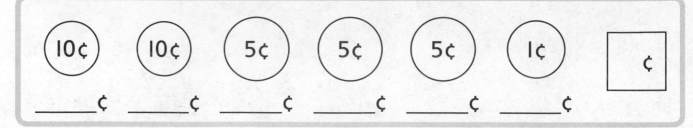

10¢	10¢	5¢	5¢	5¢	1¢	¢
_____ ¢	_____ ¢	_____ ¢	_____ ¢	_____ ¢	_____ ¢	

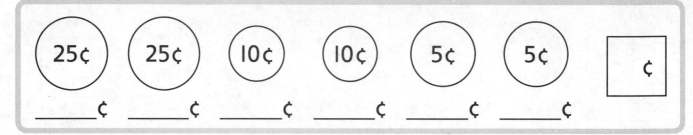

25¢	25¢	10¢	10¢	5¢	5¢	¢
_____ ¢	_____ ¢	_____ ¢	_____ ¢	_____ ¢	_____ ¢	

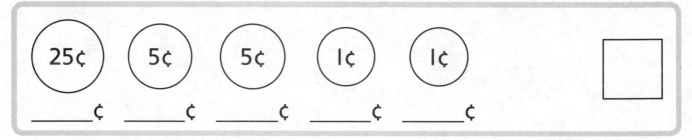

25¢	5¢	5¢	1¢	1¢	
_____ ¢	_____ ¢	_____ ¢	_____ ¢	_____ ¢	

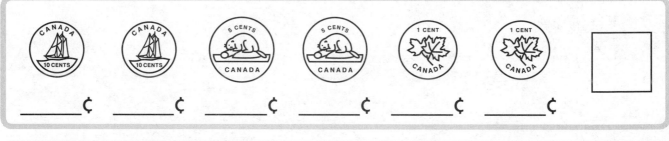

_____ ¢   _____ ¢   _____ ¢   _____ ¢   _____ ¢   _____ ¢

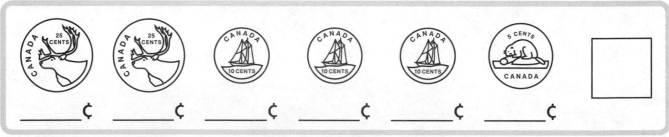

_____ ¢   _____ ¢   _____ ¢   _____ ¢   _____ ¢   _____ ¢

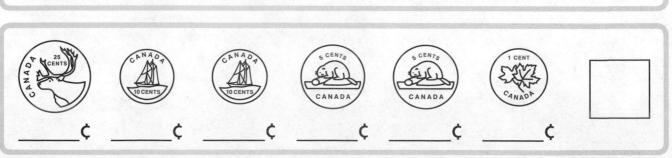

_____ ¢   _____ ¢   _____ ¢   _____ ¢   _____ ¢   _____ ¢

☐ Write the coin values from largest to smallest.
☐ Count the money.

    ⬜

 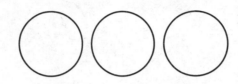 ⬜

  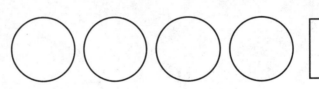 ⬜

    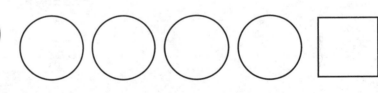 ⬜

Jake has 3 quarters and 2 dimes.
How many cents does he have?

      ⬜

Bonus
Sindi has 2 quarters, 3 dimes, and 2 nickels.
How much money does she have? ⬜

Estimating and Counting Money

☐ Estimate the amount of money.
☐ Circle groups of 10¢ using blue.
☐ Count the money.

Estimate: ___40___ ¢

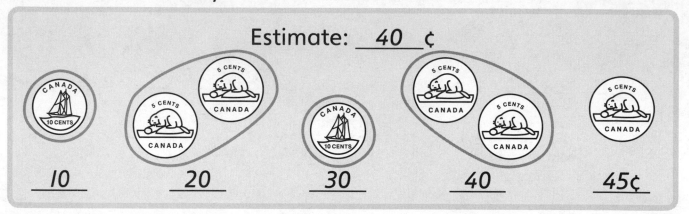

_10_   _20_   _30_   _40_   _45¢_

Estimate: _____ ¢

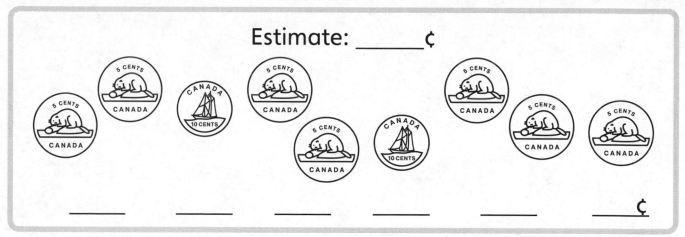

___ ___ ___ ___ ___ ___ ___ ___ ¢

☐ Estimate the amount of money.
☐ Circle groups of 25¢ using red.
☐ Count the money.

Estimate: _____ ¢

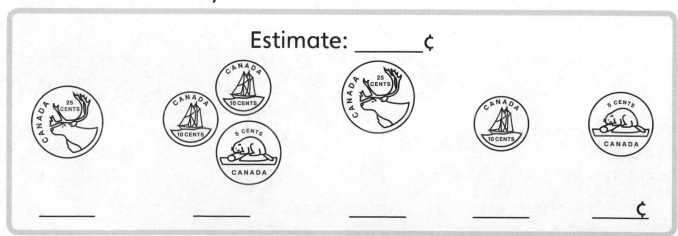

___   ___   ___   ___ ¢

☐ Estimate how much money.
☐ Circle all groups of 25¢ using red.
☐ Then circle all groups of 10¢ using blue.
☐ Count the money.

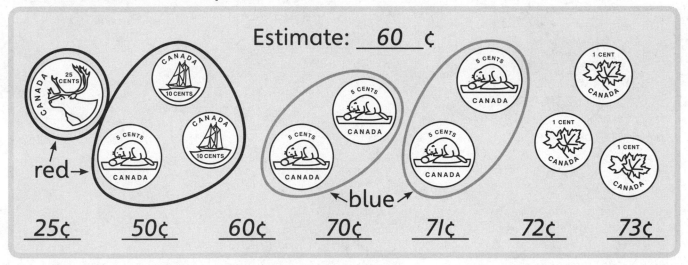

Estimate: __60__ ¢

red→

←blue→

__25¢__ __50¢__ __60¢__ __70¢__ __71¢__ __72¢__ __73¢__

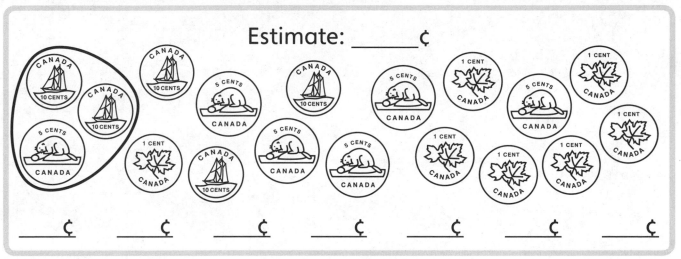

Estimate: _____ ¢

___¢ ___¢ ___¢ ___¢ ___¢ ___¢ ___¢

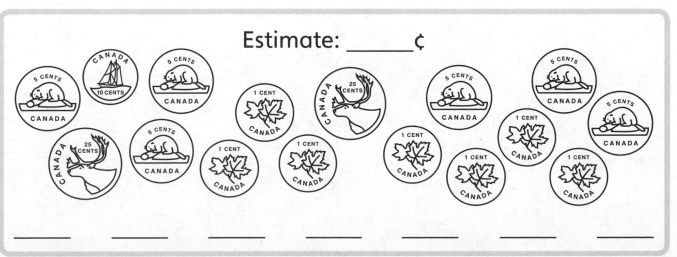

Estimate: _____ ¢

_____ _____ _____ _____ _____

Does Aputik have enough money?

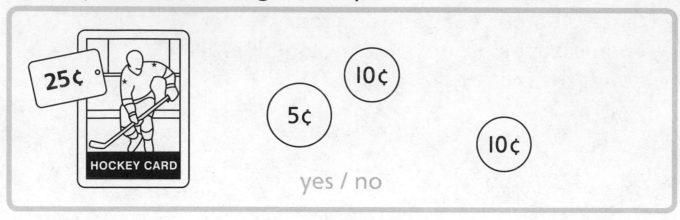

yes / no

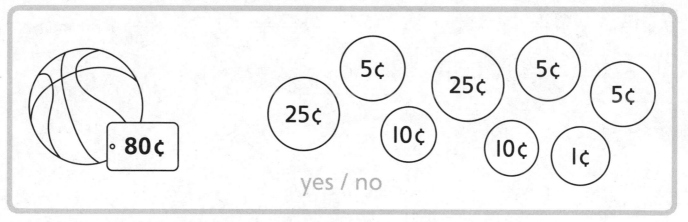

yes / no

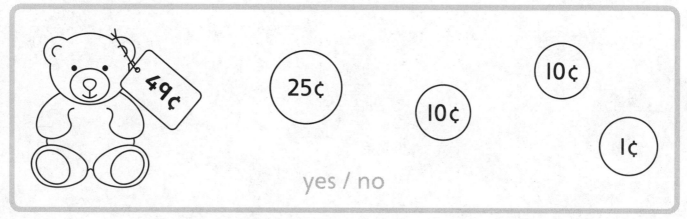

yes / no

yes / no

☐ Draw coins to make 12¢.

Use 3 coins.	Use 4 coins.

☐ Draw coins to make 27¢.

Use 3 coins.	Use 5 coins.

Use 6 coins.	Use 7 coins.

☐ Make each amount using the fewest coins.
   8¢   15¢   20¢   60¢   82¢
☐ Show how many different ways you can make 30¢ using
   dimes and nickels.

Adding Money

☐ Mary adds coins to her bag.
   How much money does she have now?

41¢   <u>51</u> ¢   <u>61</u> ¢   <u>66</u> ¢

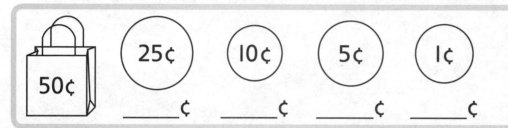

50¢   25¢   10¢   5¢   1¢

____ ¢   ____ ¢   ____ ¢   ____ ¢

35¢   10¢   10¢   5¢   5¢   5¢   1¢

____ ¢   ____ ¢   ____ ¢   ____ ¢   ____ ¢   ____ ¢

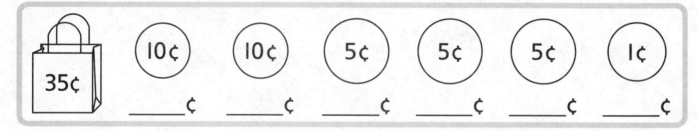

25¢

____ ¢   ____ ¢   ____ ¢   ____ ¢   ____ ¢   ____ ¢

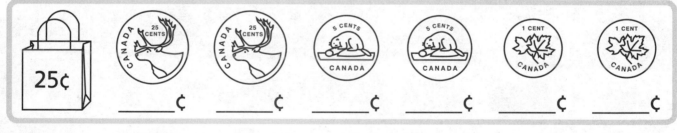

38¢

____ ¢   ____ ¢   ____ ¢   ____ ¢   ____ ¢   ____ ¢

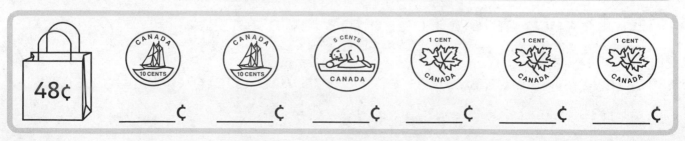

48¢

____ ¢   ____ ¢   ____ ¢   ____ ¢   ____ ¢   ____ ¢

☐ Braden adds coins to his bag.
How much money does he have now?

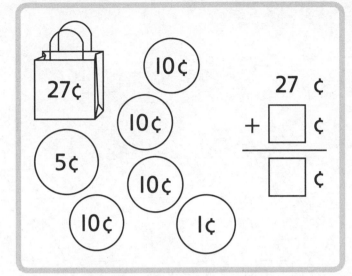

$$\begin{array}{r} 27\ \text{¢} \\ +\ \square\ \text{¢} \\ \hline \square\ \text{¢} \end{array}$$

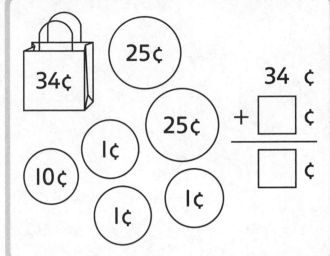

$$\begin{array}{r} 34\ \text{¢} \\ +\ \square\ \text{¢} \\ \hline \square\ \text{¢} \end{array}$$

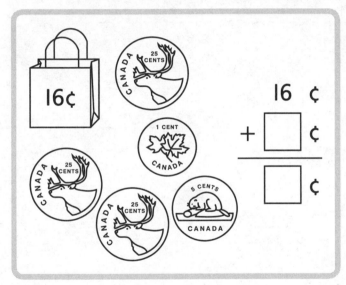

$$\begin{array}{r} 16\ \text{¢} \\ +\ \square\ \text{¢} \\ \hline \square\ \text{¢} \end{array}$$

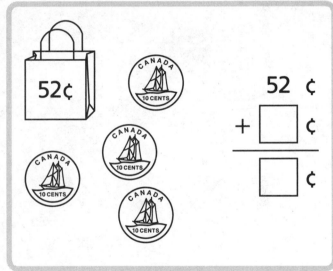

$$\begin{array}{r} 52\ \text{¢} \\ +\ \square\ \text{¢} \\ \hline \square\ \text{¢} \end{array}$$

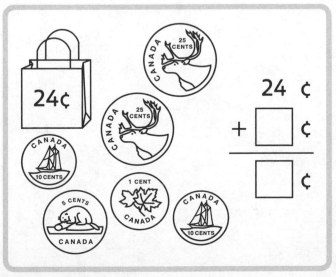

$$\begin{array}{r} 24\ \text{¢} \\ +\ \square\ \text{¢} \\ \hline \square\ \text{¢} \end{array}$$

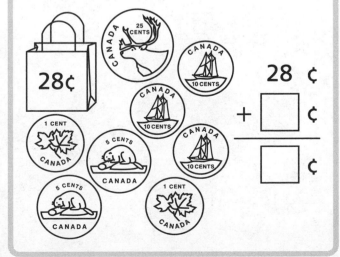

$$\begin{array}{r} 28\ \text{¢} \\ +\ \square\ \text{¢} \\ \hline \square\ \text{¢} \end{array}$$

Subtracting Money

☐ Kim pays for stickers.
How much money does she get back?

25¢ $-$ 12¢ $=$ 13¢

She gets 13¢ back.

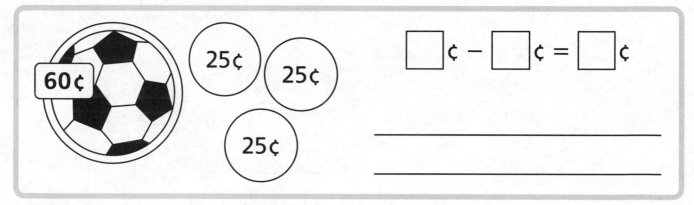

☐¢ $-$ ☐¢ $=$ ☐¢

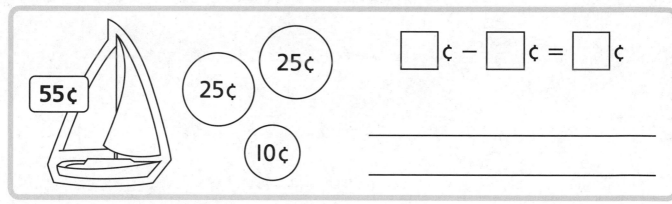

☐¢ $-$ ☐¢ $=$ ☐¢

Bonus

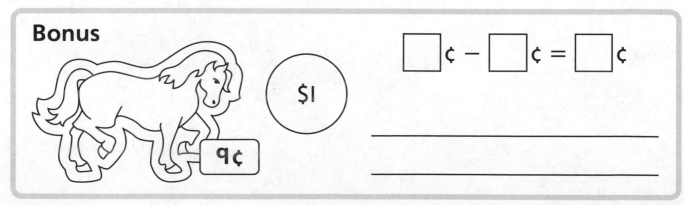

☐¢ $-$ ☐¢ $=$ ☐¢

Number Sense 2-74

☐ Write an addition or subtraction sentence.
☐ Solve the problem.

Jasmin has 15¢.

She finds 3 dimes.

Jasmin now has _____¢.

$$\begin{array}{r} 15 \\ +\ 30 \\ \hline 45 \end{array}$$

Jun has 60¢.

He gives his sister a quarter.

Jun has _____¢ left.

Glen has 2 dimes and 3 nickels.

Ronin has 2 quarters.

Ronin has _____¢ more than Glen.

Eddy has 3 nickels and 1 dime.

Kate has 2 quarters.

Eddy and Kate have _____¢ altogether.

Fractions

☐ Write **half**, **third**, **fourth**, or **fifth**.

There are two equal parts.

Each part is a ___*half*___.

There are **th**ree equal parts.

Each part is a _____.

There are **four** equal parts.

Each part is a _____.

There are **five** equal parts.

Each part is a _____.

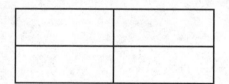

Each part is a _____.

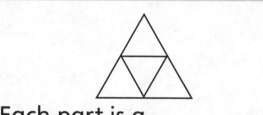

Each part is a _____.

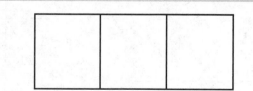

Each part is a _____.

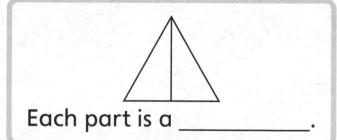

Each part is a _____.

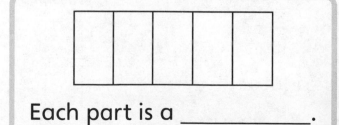

Each part is a _____.

Each part is a _____.

☐ Colour the fraction.

two thirds

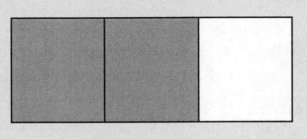

one half

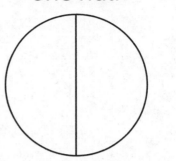

one third

three fifths

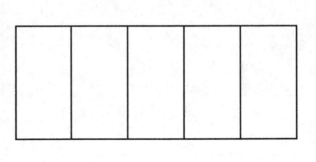

three fourths

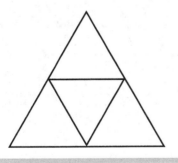

two thirds

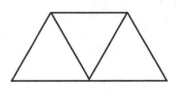

two fourths

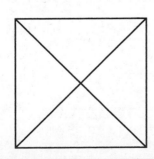

four fifths

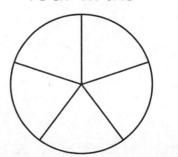

□ ✓ what is true and ✗ what is not true.
Does the picture have three fourths shaded?

✓ 3 parts are shaded.
✓ There are 4 parts in total.
_no_ ✗ All parts are the same size.

□ 3 parts are shaded.
□ There are 4 parts in total.
_____ □ All parts are the same size.

□ 3 parts are shaded.
□ There are 4 parts in total.
_____ □ All parts are the same size.

□ 3 parts are shaded.
□ There are 4 parts in total.
_____ □ All parts are the same size.

□ Does the picture ⬤ have two fifths shaded?
Explain how you know.

Writing Fractions

How many parts are shaded?
How many parts are there in total?
What fraction is shaded?

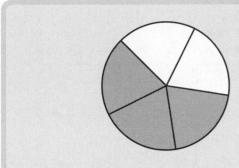

___3___ parts shaded

___5___ parts in total

$$\frac{3}{5}$$

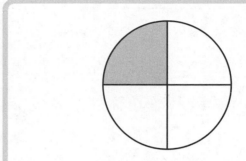

_____ parts shaded

_____ parts in total

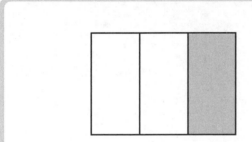

_____ parts shaded

_____ parts in total

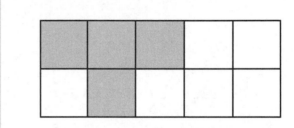

_____ parts shaded

_____ parts in total

_____ parts shaded

_____ parts in total

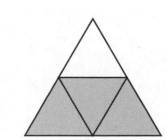

_____ parts shaded

_____ parts in total

☐ What fraction is dotted? Write the fraction in 2 ways.

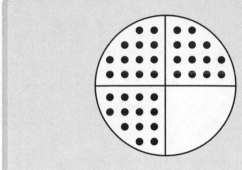

three fourths

$\frac{3}{4}$

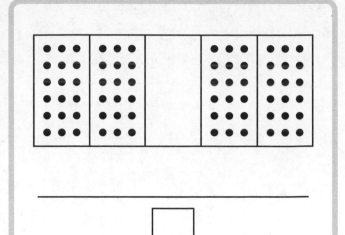

☐

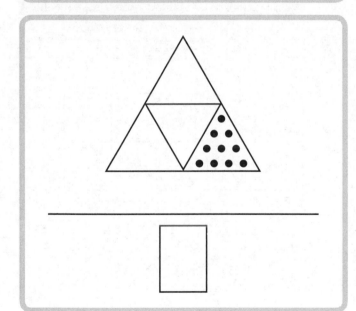

☐

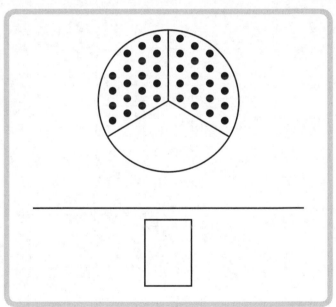

☐

☐ Write the fraction.

one third = $\frac{1}{3}$

three fifths = ☐

four fifths = ☐

two fourths = ☐

one half = ☐

two fifths = ☐

Comparing Fractions

Who ate more pizza?

Bella ate $\frac{1}{2}$ Jay ate $\frac{1}{4}$

_____ ate more pizza.

Ray ate $\frac{1}{6}$ Mary ate $\frac{1}{4}$

_____ ate more pizza.

☐ Colour I part in each picture.
☐ Write **more** or **less**.

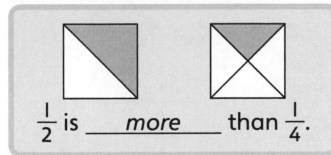

$\frac{1}{2}$ is ___*more*___ than $\frac{1}{4}$.

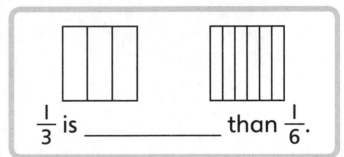

$\frac{1}{3}$ is _____ than $\frac{1}{6}$.

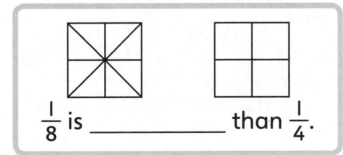

$\frac{1}{8}$ is _____ than $\frac{1}{4}$.

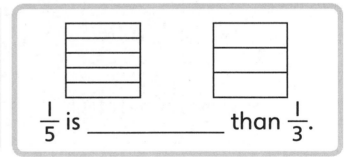

$\frac{1}{5}$ is _____ than $\frac{1}{3}$.

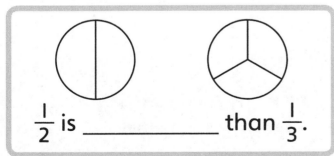

$\frac{1}{2}$ is _____ than $\frac{1}{3}$.

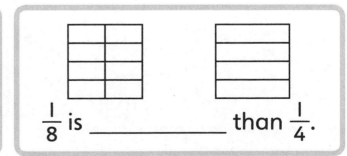

$\frac{1}{8}$ is _____ than $\frac{1}{4}$.

☐ Circle the 2 questions that compared the same fractions.
Did you get the same answer? _____

☐ Fill the measuring cups with the correct amount.
☐ Circle the cup that is more full.
☐ Write **more** or **less**.

one half full   one third full

One half is _____more_____ than one third.

one fifth full   one third full

One fifth is _____ than one third.

one fourth full   one tenth full

One fourth is _____ than one tenth.

☐ Dividing something into more parts makes each part

_____.
smaller / bigger

What fraction does each picture show?
Which fraction is more?

two thirds

three fourths

Three fourths is more than two thirds.

More Than One Whole

Hanna cut pizzas into fourths.

11 pieces are shaded.

11 fourths or $\frac{11}{4}$ are shaded.

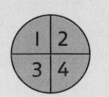 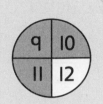

What fraction is shaded?

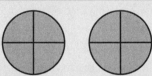

___9___ fourths $\dfrac{9}{4}$

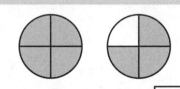

_____ fourths $\dfrac{}{4}$

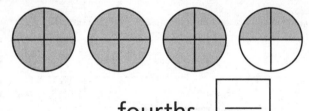

_____ fourths $\dfrac{}{4}$

_____ eighths $\dfrac{}{8}$

_____ $\dfrac{}{6}$

_____ $\dfrac{}{}$

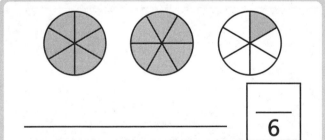   

_____ $\dfrac{}{}$

How many parts are shaded to make 1 whole?

 $1 = \dfrac{\Box}{4}$

 $1 = \dfrac{\Box}{6}$

 $1 = \dfrac{\Box}{3}$

 $1 = \dfrac{\Box}{8}$

 $1 = \dfrac{\Box}{12}$

$1 = \dfrac{\Box}{20}$

▢ Write the missing number.

$1 = \dfrac{\Box}{5}$

$1 = \dfrac{\Box}{7}$

$1 = \dfrac{\Box}{10}$

$1 = \dfrac{9}{\Box}$

$1 = \dfrac{11}{\Box}$

$1 = \dfrac{17}{\Box}$

Bonus

$$1 = \dfrac{19}{\Box} = \dfrac{\Box}{16} = \dfrac{15}{\Box} = \dfrac{\Box}{21}$$

How many whole pies are shaded?

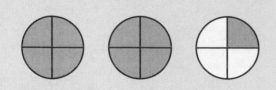

_2_ whole pies

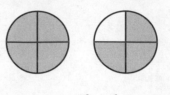

_____ whole pie

_____ whole pies

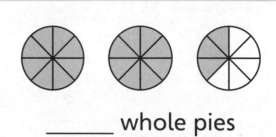

_____ whole pies

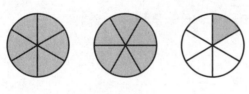

_____ whole pies

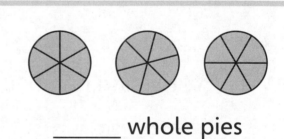

_____ whole pies

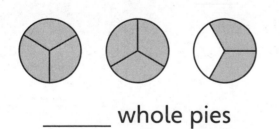

_____ whole pies

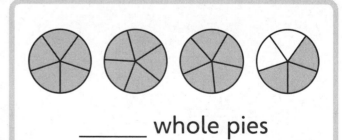

_____ whole pies

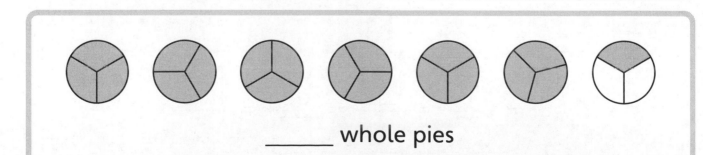

_____ whole pies

Hanna and her friends cut pizzas into fourths.

They have 2 and three fourths of a pizza left.

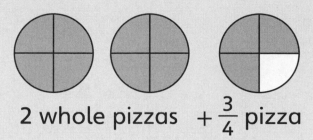

2 whole pizzas $+ \frac{3}{4}$ pizza

How much pizza is left?

2 and one fourth

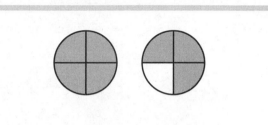

_____

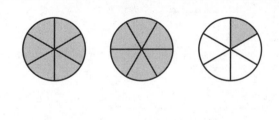

_____

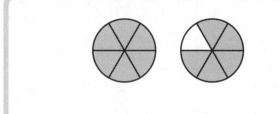

_____

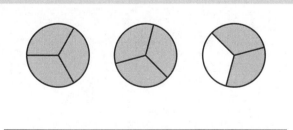

_____

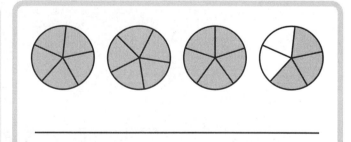

_____

Bonus

_____

Multiplication

$$2 + 2 + 2 + 2 + 2 \;=\; 5 \times 2 \;=\; 5 \text{ times } 2$$

☐ Write the addition as multiplication.

$2 + 2 + 2 + 2 = \underline{\hspace{1.2cm}} \times 2$

$2 + 2 + 2 = \underline{\hspace{1.2cm}} \times 2$

$2 + 2 + 2 + 2 + 2 + 2 + 2 + 2 + 2 = \underline{\hspace{1.2cm}} \times 2$

$3 + 3 + 3 + 3 + 3 + 3 = \underline{\hspace{1.2cm}} \times 3$

$7 + 7 + 7 + 7 + 7 + 7 = \underline{\hspace{1.2cm}} \times \underline{\hspace{1.2cm}}$

$8 + 8 + 8 + 8 + 8 + 8 = \underline{\hspace{1.2cm}} \times \underline{\hspace{1.2cm}}$

$12 + 12 + 12 + 12 + 12 + 12 + 12 = \underline{\hspace{1.2cm}} \times \underline{\hspace{1.2cm}}$

$100 + 100 + 100 = \underline{\hspace{1.2cm}} \times \underline{\hspace{1.2cm}}$

$10 + 10 + 10 + 10 + 10 + 10 + 10 + 10 = \underline{\hspace{1.2cm}} \times \underline{\hspace{1.2cm}}$

☐ Multiply by counting the dots.

$$\begin{array}{r} 4 \\ +\ 4 \\ \hline \end{array}$$
2 × 4 = ☐

rows → ↑ in each row

$$\begin{array}{r} 6 \\ +\ 6 \\ \hline \end{array}$$
2 × 6 = ☐

$$\begin{array}{r} 4 \\ 4 \\ +\ 4 \\ \hline \end{array}$$
3 × 4 = ☐

$$\begin{array}{r} 3 \\ 3 \\ +\ 3 \\ \hline \end{array}$$
3 × 3 = ☐

$$\begin{array}{r} 7 \\ +\ 7 \\ \hline \end{array}$$
2 × 7 = ☐

$$\begin{array}{r} 3 \\ 3 \\ 3 \\ +\ 3 \\ \hline \end{array}$$
4 × 3 = ☐

☐ Draw the dots, then multiply.

$$\begin{array}{r} 2 \\ 2 \\ +\ 2 \\ \hline \end{array}$$
3 × 2 = ☐

$$\begin{array}{r} 5 \\ +\ 5 \\ \hline \end{array}$$
2 × 5 = ☐

☐ Cover the grid to multiply.

$2 \times 3 =$ _____

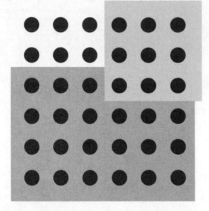

$4 \times 2 =$ _____

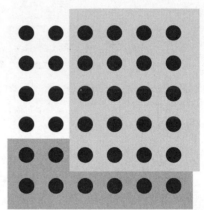

$5 \times 2 =$ _____

$4 \times 1 =$ _____

$1 \times 6 =$ _____

$2 \times 6 =$ _____

$4 \times 3 =$ _____

$3 \times 2 =$ _____

$2 \times 5 =$ _____

$3 \times 6 =$ _____

$4 \times 4 =$ _____

$3 \times 3 =$ _____

Multiplying by Skip Counting

☐ Keep track as you go along.

| 6 | 9 | 12 | 15 |

$5 \times 3 = \underline{3} + \underline{3} + \underline{3} + \underline{3} + \underline{3} = \boxed{15}$

☐ ☐ ☐

$4 \times 5 = \underline{} + \underline{} + \underline{} + \underline{} = \boxed{}$

☐ ☐ ☐ ☐ ☐

$6 \times 10 = \underline{} + \underline{} + \underline{} + \underline{} + \underline{} + \underline{} = \boxed{}$

☐ ☐ ☐ ☐ ☐

$6 \times 2 = \underline{} + \underline{} + \underline{} + \underline{} + \underline{} + \underline{} = \boxed{}$

☐ ☐ ☐ ☐

$5 \times 4 = \underline{} + \underline{} + \underline{} + \underline{} + \underline{} = \boxed{}$

☐ ☐ ☐

$4 \times 3 = \underline{} + \underline{} + \underline{} + \underline{} = \boxed{}$

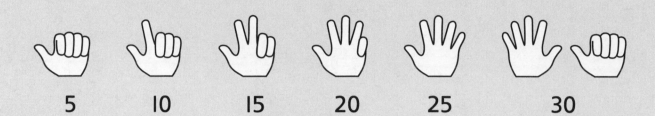

5   10   15   20   25   30

☐ Multiply.

3 × 5 = _____	4 × 5 = _____	5 × 5 = _____
1 × 5 = _____	6 × 5 = _____	9 × 5 = _____

☐ Count by 3s.

_3_ ___ ___ ___ ___ ___ ___

☐ Multiply.

2 × 3 = _____	4 × 3 = _____	1 × 3 = _____
6 × 3 = _____	3 × 3 = _____	10 × 3 = _____

Division

3 friends want to share 6 apples equally.

Each friend takes 1 apple.

Each friend can take another apple.

Each friend gets 2 apples.

☐ Put 1 apple in each basket until all the apples are shared.
Draw circles for apples.

How many does each person get?

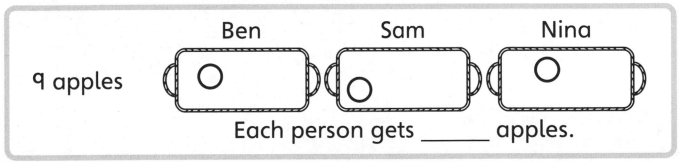

Ben   Sam   Nina

9 apples

Each person gets _____ apples.

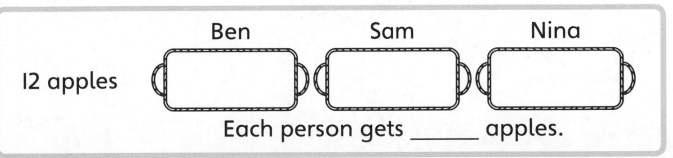

Ben   Sam   Nina

12 apples

Each person gets _____ apples.

2 friends want to share apples.

☐ Put the same number of apples in each basket.

☐ Finish the division sentence.

 **6 apples**

number of apples → $\boxed{6} \div 2 = \boxed{}$ ← number in each basket

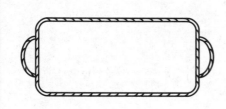 **10 apples**

$\boxed{} \div 2 = \boxed{}$

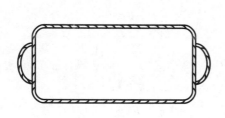 **8 apples**

$\boxed{} \div 2 = \boxed{}$

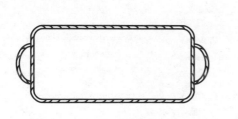 **12 apples**

$\boxed{} \div 2 = \boxed{}$

☐ Put the same number of apples in each basket.
☐ Write the division sentence.

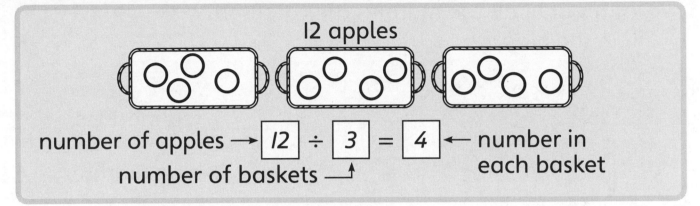

12 apples

number of apples → $12 ÷ 3 = 4$ ← number in each basket

number of baskets →

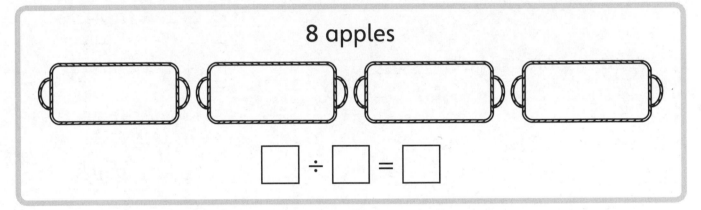

8 apples

☐ ÷ ☐ = ☐

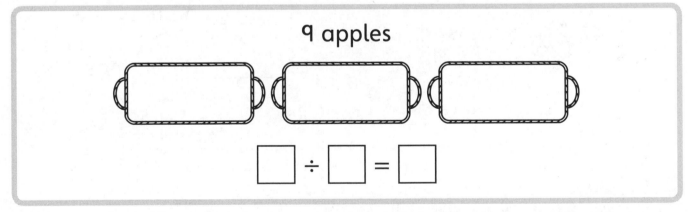

9 apples

☐ ÷ ☐ = ☐

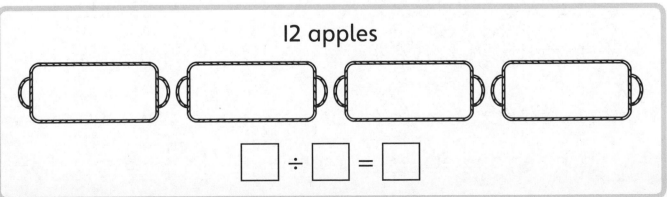

12 apples

☐ ÷ ☐ = ☐

☐ Divide the marbles equally.
☐ Colour I marble red, I marble blue, and I marble green.
   Do this until all the marbles are coloured.
☐ Fill in the blanks.

 ☺ _____ red marbles

☺ _____ blue marbles

☺ _____ green marbles

Each person gets _____ marbles.   ☐ ÷ 3 = ☐

 ☺ _____ red marbles

☺ _____ blue marbles

☺ _____ green marbles

Each person gets _____ marbles.   ☐ ÷ 3 = ☐

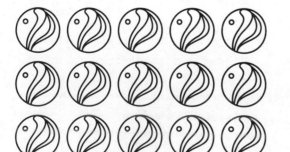 ☺ _____ red marbles

☺ _____ blue marbles

☺ _____ green marbles

Each person gets _____ marbles.   ☐ ÷ 3 = ☐

     Number Sense 2-81

How Many Groups?

☐ Divide the people into groups of 3.

How many groups? _____

How many groups? _____

How many groups? _____

How many groups? _____

How many groups? _____

Number Sense 2-82

☐ Find how many groups.

How many groups of 2? ___4___

How many groups of 5? _____

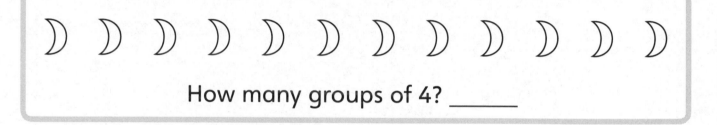

How many groups of 4? _____

How many groups of 2? _____

How many groups of 4? _____

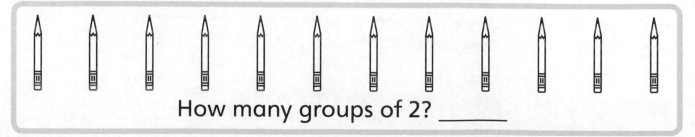

How many groups of 2? _____

Measuring Time

☐ Sing the alphabet as your partner does the activity.
☐ Write the letter you get to when your partner finishes.

5 jumping jacks  _J_	spins around 3 times  ___
traces these shapes 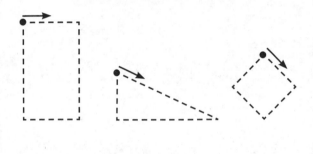 ___	stands up and sits down ___
writes "hello" backwards  ___	writes their name backwards  ___

What took the longest time? _____

What took the shortest time? _____

☐ Draw or describe your measuring unit.

[blank box]

☐ Measure using your own unit.

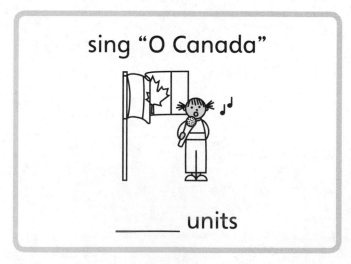

stand up and sit down

_____ units

write the alphabet

ABC

_____ units

sing "O Canada"

_____ units

read a story

_____ units

📓 Is your measuring unit better for measuring tasks that take a long time or short time? Explain.

Clock Faces

 This is a clock face.

Numbers start at I and end at I2.

☐ Fill in the missing 3, 6, 9, and I2.

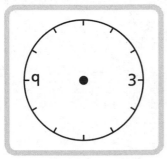   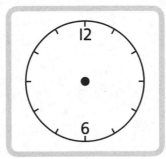   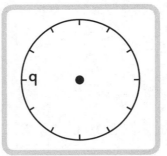   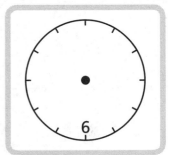

☐ Fill in the missing numbers. Start with 3, 6, 9, and I2.

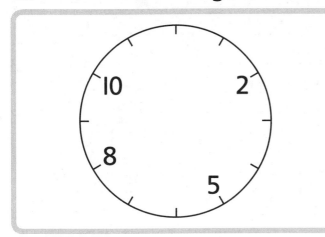   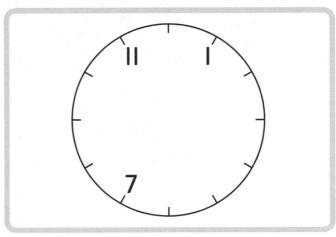

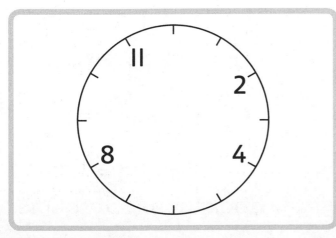   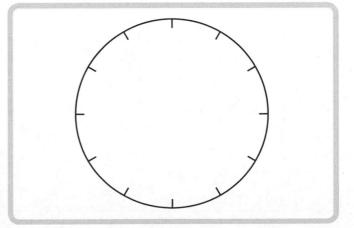

Measuring Time with Clocks

Start when the fast hand is at 12.

☐ Draw the fast hand when you finish.

write your name: _____

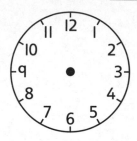

erase your name

say the alphabet

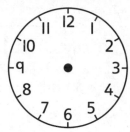

count to 30

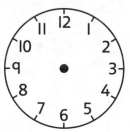

order the numbers

___ ___ ___ ___ ___ ___

27	34
16	52
81	45

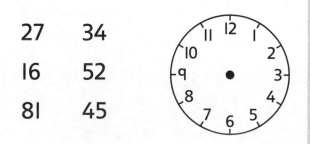

order the numbers

___ ___ ___ ___ ___ ___

84	82
86	81
89	87

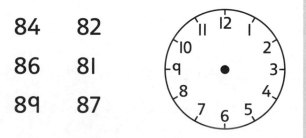

_____ took the longest time.

_____ took the shortest time.

Josh starts juggling.

Then he drops the balls.

How long does Josh juggle?

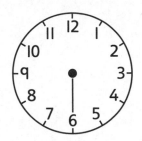   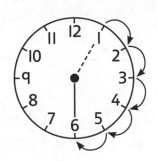

starts   stops   Josh juggles for _____

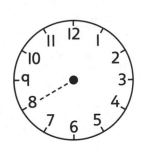      

starts   stops   Josh juggles for _____

☐ Did Josh get better on his second try? Explain your answer.

_____

_____

_____

_____

Time to the Hour

The **hour hand** is short and thick.

☐ Circle the hour hand.

Measurement 2-24

When the minute hand points at 12, we say "**o'clock**."

o'clock   not o'clock

☐ Is it o'clock? Write **yes** or **no**.

_____

_____

_____

_____

_____

_____

_____

_____

_____

A **digital clock** shows the time with numbers only.

When the digital clock shows :00 minutes, we say "**o'clock**."

hours : minutes

☐ Is it o'clock? Write **yes** or **no**.

 6:00	10:30	3:00
yes	_no_	___

4:00	2:00	11:15
___	___	___

 9:00   It is **9 o'clock** or **9:00**.

☐ Write the time another way.

1:00	8:00	10:00
1 o'clock	___	___

11 o'clock	7 o'clock	6 o'clock
_11:00_	___	___

Measurement 2-24

 It is **9 o'clock** or **9:00**.

☐ Write the time in two ways.

___6___ o'clock

___6___ :00

_____ o'clock

_____ :00

_____ o'clock

_____ :00

_____

____ : ____

_____

____ : ____

_____

____ : ____

☐ Use a toy clock to show these times.
☐ Circle the two that are the same.

7:00	3 o'clock	5:00
1:00	6 o'clock	1 o'clock

Half Past

☐ Write the time.

half past __7__

half past _____

half past _____

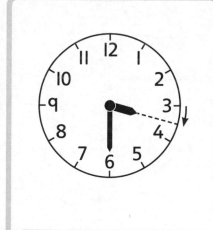

_____

_____

_____

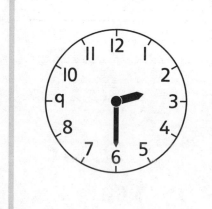

_____

_____

_____

☐ What time is it?

half past 10

7 o'clock

_____

_____

_____

_____

_____

_____

_____

_____

_____

_____

_____

_____

_____

_____

Time to the Half Hour

How many minutes after 10:00?

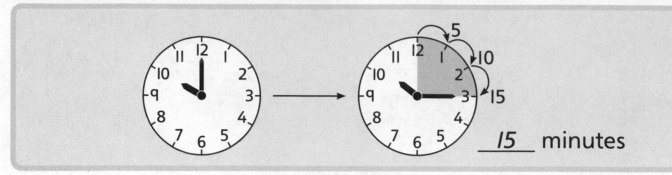

_____15_____ minutes

_____ minutes
after 10:00

_____ minutes
after 10:00

_____ minutes
after 10:00

☐ Write the time.

_____15_____ minutes

after ___7:00___

is ___7___ : ___15___

_____ minutes

after _____

is _____ : _____

_____ minutes

after _____

is _____ : _____

Measurement 2-26

It is half an hour after 8:00 or 30 minutes after 8:00.

half past 8　　　　　　**8:30**

☐ Write the time in two ways.

half past _____

_____ :30

half past _____

_____ :30

half past _____

_____ :30

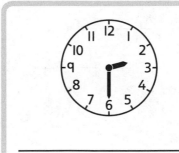

_____

_____ : _____

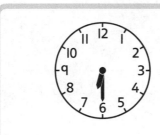

_____

_____ : _____

_____

_____ : _____

☐ Use a toy clock to show these times.
☐ Circle the two that are the same.

12:30	half past 2	4:30
5:30	half past 9	half past 12

☐ Write the time.

__half past 2__

_____

__4 o'clock__

_____

_____

_____

_____

_____

_____

_____

_____

_____

_____

_____

_____

_____

Quarter Past

It is a quarter of an hour after 7:00 or 15 minutes after 7:00.

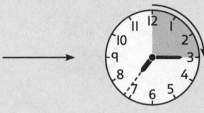

quarter past 7   7:15

☐ Write the time in two ways.

quarter past __1__

___1___ : __15__

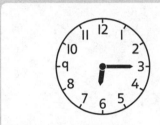

quarter past ____

____ : ____

quarter past ____

____ : ____

_____

____ : ____

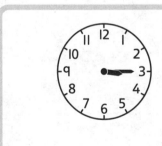

_____

____ : ____

_____

____ : ____

☐ Use a toy clock to show these times.
☐ Circle the two that are the same.

11:15	quarter past 7	quarter past 2
quarter past 9	8:15	7:15

Quarter To

It is 3 quarters of an hour after 4:00

or

a quarter of an hour before 5:00.

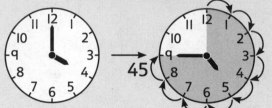  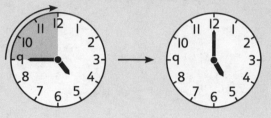

45 minutes after 4:00 or 4:45

quarter to 5

quarter to _____

quarter to _____

quarter to _____

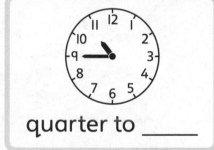 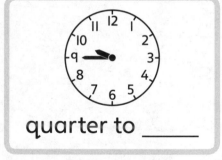 

quarter to _____

quarter to _____

quarter to _____

```
2:45
```
quarter to _____

```
7:45
```
quarter to _____

```
8:45
```
quarter to _____

```
3:45
```
quarter to _____

```
9:45
```
quarter to _____

```
6:45
```
quarter to _____

☐ Circle the times that are the same.

A quarter of an hour **before** 4:00 is **quarter to** 4.
A quarter of an hour **after** 4:00 is **quarter past** 4.

quarter to 4   4:00   quarter past 4

⬜ Write the time.

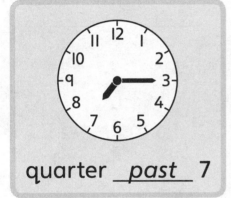

quarter __*past*__ 7

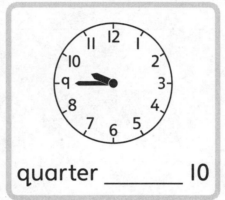

quarter _____ 10

quarter _____ 5

quarter _____

quarter _____

quarter _____

_____

_____

_____

Measurement 2-28

☐ Write the time in two ways.

   7   :   45

quarter to 8

_____ : _____

_____

_____ : _____

_____

_____

_____

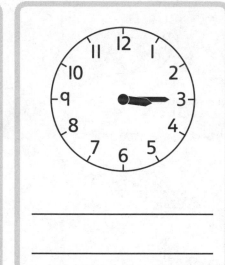

_____

_____

_____

_____

_____

_____

_____

_____

_____

_____

Bar Graphs

How many?

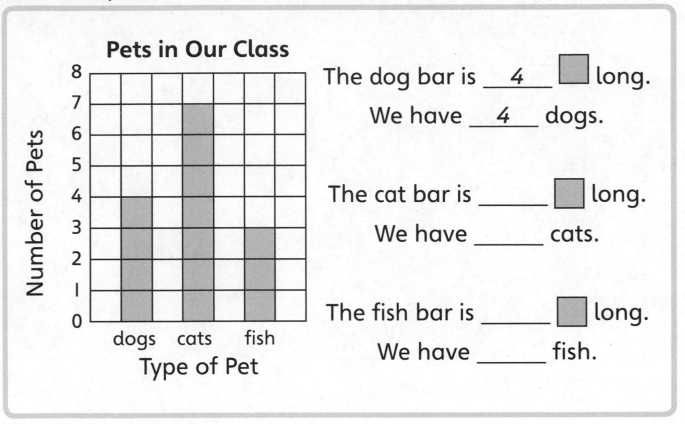

Pets in Our Class

The dog bar is ___4___ ▢ long.

We have ___4___ dogs.

The cat bar is _____ ▢ long.

We have _____ cats.

The fish bar is _____ ▢ long.

We have _____ fish.

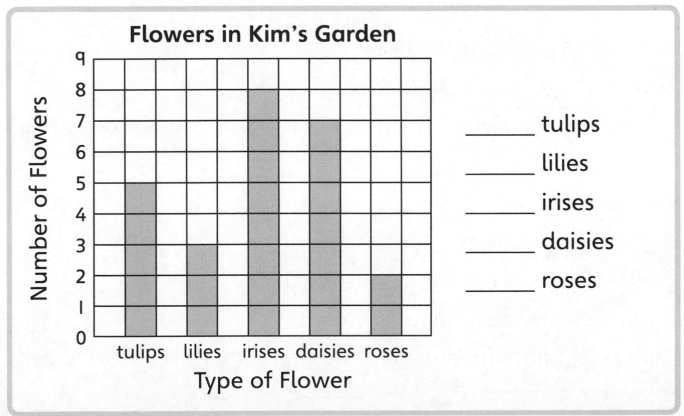

Flowers in Kim's Garden

_____ tulips

_____ lilies

_____ irises

_____ daisies

_____ roses

Probability and Data Management 2-8

☐ Use the bar graph to answer the questions.

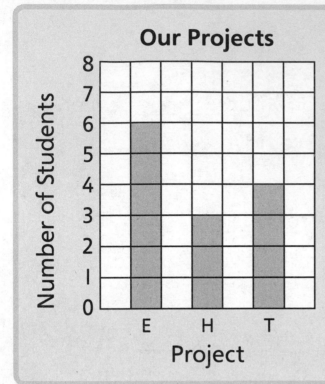

E - Earthquakes

H - Hurricanes

T - Tornadoes

How many students chose each project?

Earthquakes _____ students

Hurricanes _____ students

Tornadoes _____ students

How many more students chose earthquakes than tornadoes?

_____ more students

How many fewer students chose hurricanes than tornadoes?

_____ fewer student

What was the most popular project? _____

What was the least popular project? _____

Hurricanes and tornadoes have strong winds. How many students chose projects about winds? _____ + _____ = _____

Use the data to finish the bar graph.
Answer the questions.

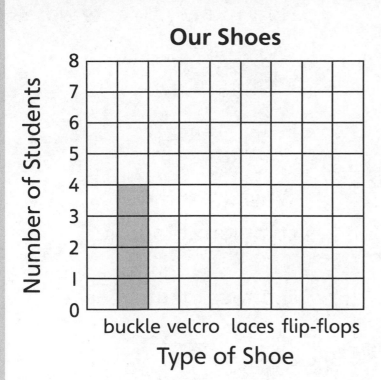

Our Shoes

Number of Students

buckle velcro laces flip-flops
Type of Shoe

buckle	4
velcro	7
laces	8
flip-flops	3

Which bar is tallest?

_____

Which bar is shortest?

_____

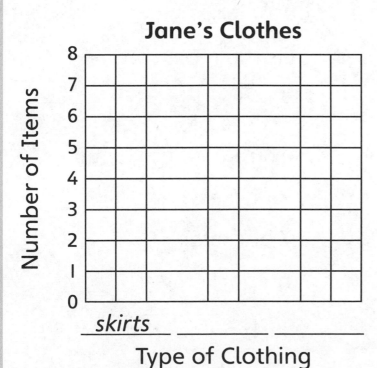

Jane's Clothes

Number of Items

skirts _____ _____
Type of Clothing

Jane has 5 skirts,
7 pants, and
3 pairs of shorts.

How many more
pants than skirts does
Jane have?

_____

Probability and Data Management 2-8

Line Plots

☐ Count the ✗s to answer the questions.

Shirts Worn Today

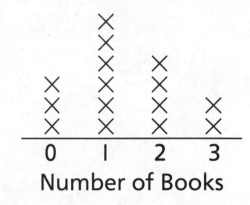

orange blue red green
Colour of Shirt

How many students wore

orange? ___4___

blue? _____

red? _____

green? _____

Which was the most

common colour? _____

Books Read This Week

X
X
X   X
X   X   X
X   X   X   X
X   X   X   X
0   I   2   3
Number of Books

How many students read

no books? _____

I book? _____

2 books? _____

3 books? _____

What is the most common

number of books read? _____

Pockets We Have Today

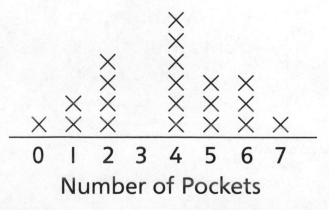

0 I 2 3 4 5 6 7
Number of Pockets

How many people have

2 pockets? _____

7 pockets? _____

no pockets? _____

Which number of pockets

does nobody have? _____

Probability and Data Management 2-9

☐ Use the line plot to answer the questions.

Length of Our Names

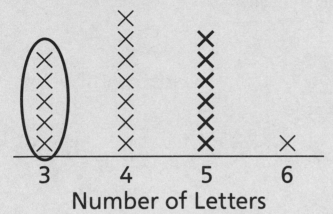

Number of Letters

5 people have 3 letters in their names.
Circle the ✕s that show this.

The thick ✕s show that
__6__ people have
__5__ letters in their names.

Buttons on Our Clothes Today

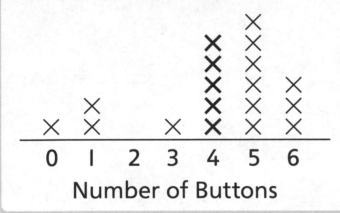

Number of Buttons

2 people have 1 button on their clothes today.
Circle the ✕s that show this.

The thick ✕s show that
_____ people have
_____ buttons today.

Size of Our Families

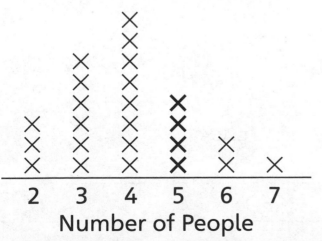

Number of People

6 people have 3 people in their families.
Circle the ✕s that show this.

The thick ✕s show that

_____

_____

_____

The line plots show the number of books read.

What is the largest number of books read?
How many people read that many books?

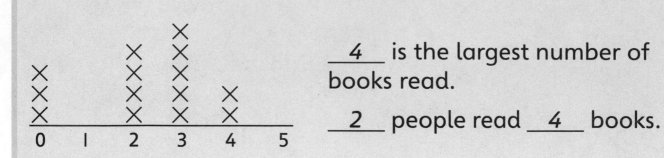

____4____ is the largest number of
books read.

____2____ people read ____4____ books.

_____ is the largest number of
books read.

_____ people read _____ books.

_____ is the largest number of
books read.

_____ people read _____ books.

_____ is the largest number of
books read.

_____

_____

Probability and Data Management 2-9

Length of Our Names

		X	X								
		X	X								
	X	X	X								
	X	X	X								
	X	X	X	X							
	X	X	X	X							
	3	4	5	6							

Number of Letters

☐ Count the number of letters in each name below.
☐ Add a blue X to the chart for **Eddy**.
☐ Add a red X to the chart for **Lewis**.
☐ Add a green X to the chart for **Jin**.
☐ Add a column and an orange X to the chart for **Yu**.
☐ Add column and a black X to the chart for **Jasmine**.
☐ Add a brown X to the chart for your name.

Siblings (Brothers or Sisters)

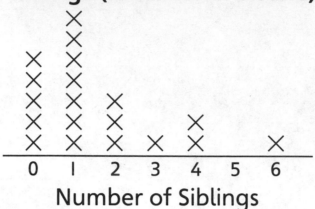

Number of Siblings

What is **the largest number** of siblings a person has?
____ siblings

How many people have that many siblings? ____ person

What is **the most common** number of siblings? ____ sibling

How many people have that many siblings? ____ people

Books We Read This Week

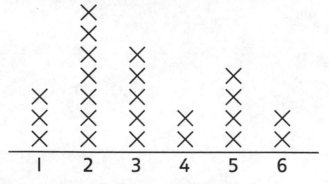

Number of Books

How many **more** people read 3 books than 4 books?
____ more people

How many **fewer** people read 6 books than 2 books?
____ fewer people read ____ books than ____ books.

Tallies

☐ Write the number or draw the tally.

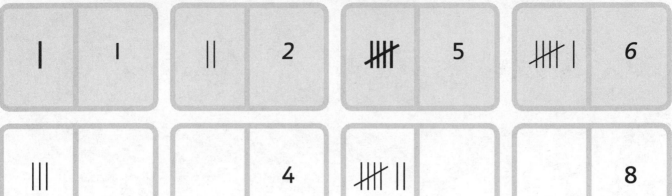

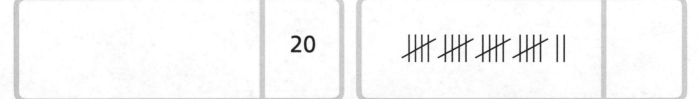

☐ Tally the number of objects.
☐ Cross out the objects as you count.

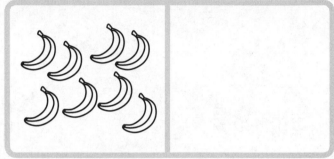

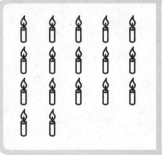

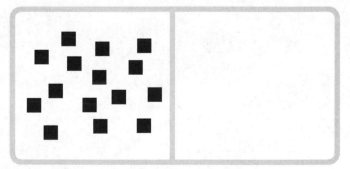

Probability and Data Management 2-10

Asking Questions about Data

☐ Ask a question about the graph using the words given.

Favourite Classes

gym	😊	😊	😊	😊	😊
art	🎨	🎨			
music	🎵	🎵	🎵		
drama	😎	😎			

how many

How many students

chose gym class?

_____

the same number

Which two classes were

chosen by the same

number of students?

two most popular

What are the two most

popular classes?

_____

Favourite Ice Cream

chocolate	卌 卌
vanilla	‖‖
strawberry	卌 ‖‖

how many

_____

_____

_____

the most popular

_____

_____

_____

the least popular

_____

_____

☐ Ask a question about the bar graph using the words given.
☐ Have a friend answer your question.

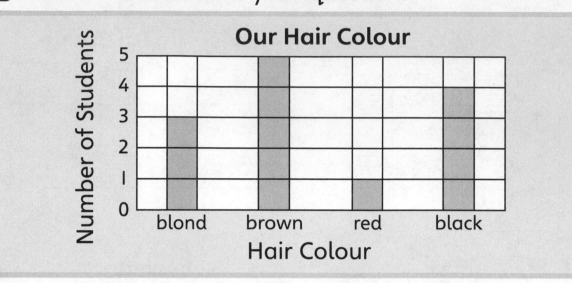

Our Hair Colour

Question: *fewer ... than*
How many fewer students have red hair
than blond hair?

Answer: _____

Question: *more ... than*
_____
_____

Answer: _____
_____

Question: *the most common*
_____
_____

Answer: _____
_____

Probability and Data Management 2-11

Surveys

Lela asked her class a question.

○	What is your favourite season?
	Spring Summer Winter

☐ Are there enough choices? yes / no

☐ Explain. _____

_____

_____

What choice should she add? _____

Fred asked his class a question.

○	How many siblings do you have?
	0 1 2 3

Don has 4 siblings.

Luc has 7 siblings.

They could not answer the survey.

☐ Add **one more** choice so that both Luc and Don can answer the survey. _____

☐ Ask students in your class: How did you get to school today?
☐ Tally your results.

Title: _____

school bus	
car	
walk	
bike	
scooter	
other	

☐ Make a pictograph with the data. Use ☺.

Title: _____

Probability and Data Management 2-12

What did you learn from your survey?

☐ What was the most common way to get to school today?

_____

☐ How many students used that way? _____

☐ Why do you think that way was the most common
way of getting to school?

_____

_____

_____

☐ What else does your pictograph show?

_____

_____

_____

☐ Write 2 questions about your data and have
a friend answer them.

Question: _____

_____

Answer: _____

_____

Question: _____

_____

Answer: _____

_____

Certain or Impossible?

Certain events always happen.	**Impossible** events never happen.
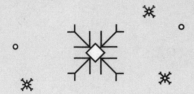 It will get cold in winter.	 An alien will join my class.

☐ Sort the events.

I will spin black on this spinner.

I will be older next year.

I will be 3 years old next year.

Certain   **Impossible**

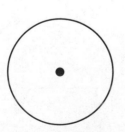

I will spin white on this spinner.

Cookies will grow on trees.

I will roll 1, 2, 3, 4, 5, or 6 on a die.

Likely or Unlikely?

Likely events happen often but not always.

I will go to school in the morning.

Unlikely events can happen but not so often.

I will roll a 3 five times in a row.

☐ Write **likely** or **unlikely**.

I will eat lunch.

_____ *likely*

I will eat cake today.

_____

I will roll a 6 ten times in a row.

_____

I will spin black on this spinner.

_____

It will snow in June.

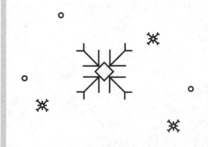

_____

I will take a white cube from this bag.

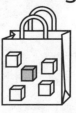

_____

Probability and Data Management 2-14

More Likely or Less Likely?

impossible   unlikely   likely   certain

☐ Circle the event that is **more** likely.

 or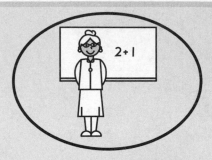

A mermaid will teach math.   Our teacher will teach math.

 or

A bird will fly.   A cow will fly.

 or

I will be hot.   I will be hot.

 or

It will rain in April.   It will snow in April.

Probability and Data Management 2-15

More Likely, Equally Likely, or Less Likely?

☐ Compare the events.

| more likely | equally likely | less likely |

Cam will ride a pony.   Cam will ride a bird.

It is more likely that Cam will ride a pony than a bird.

A fish will sing.   Avril will sing.

It is _____ likely that a fish will sing than _____.

A coin will land on heads.   A coin will land on tails.

It is _____.

I will pull out a grey cube.   I will pull out a white cube.

_____

Comparing Areas

☐ Trace the shapes.
☐ Cut them out and compare the areas.
☐ Write **bigger** and **smaller** on each pair.

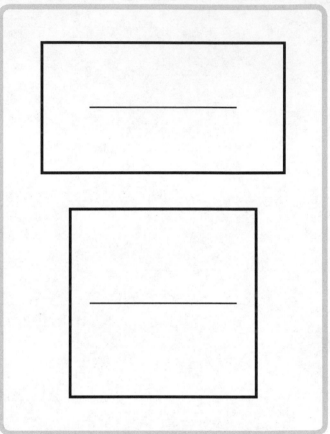

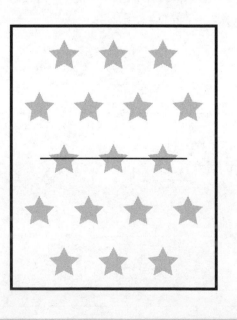

Measuring Area

Use big 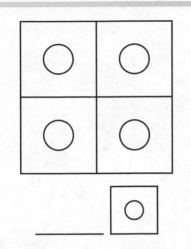 as a unit.

☐ Measure the area.

_____

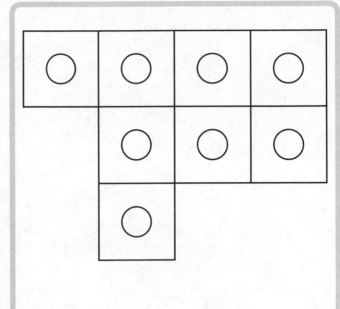

_____

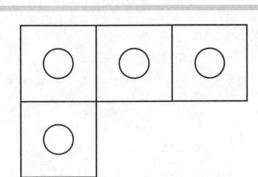

_____

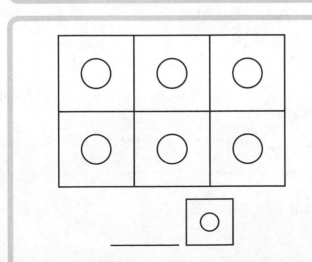

_____

Use big 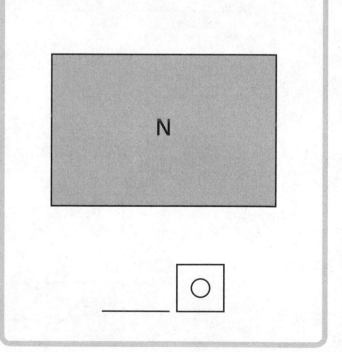 as a unit.

☐ Measure the area.

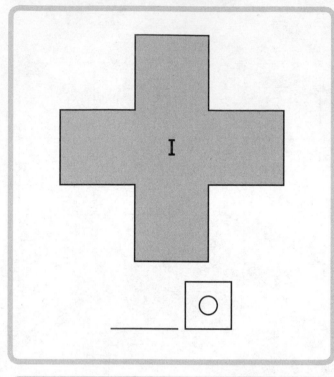

I

___ ☐○

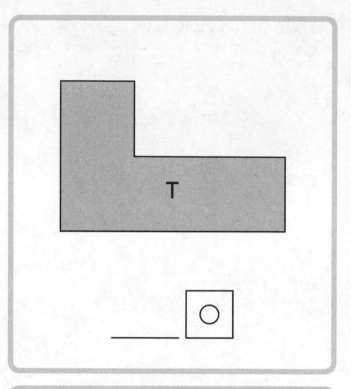

T

___ ☐○

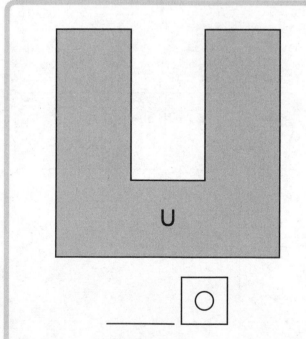

U

___ ☐○

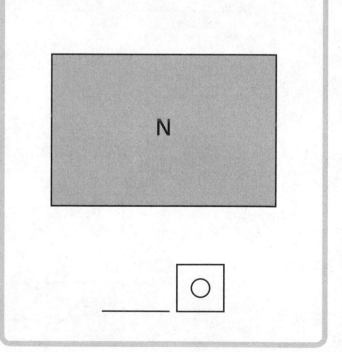

N

___ ☐○

☐ Order the shapes from biggest to smallest.

____ ____ ____ ____

☐ Estimate the area in big 🎲.
☐ Measure the area to check.

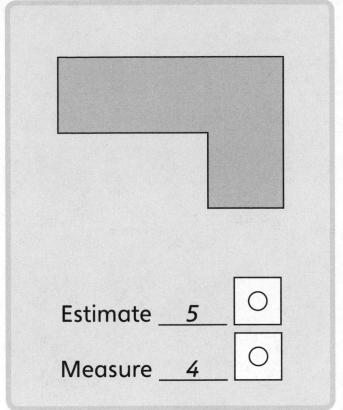

Estimate ___5___ ⬜○

Measure ___4___ ⬜○

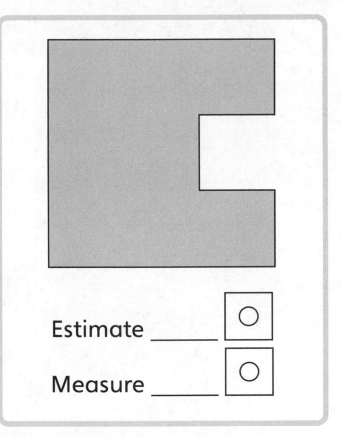

Estimate _____ ⬜○

Measure _____ ⬜○

Estimate _____ ⬜○

Measure _____ ⬜○

Use ▭ as a unit.

☐ Estimate the area.
☐ Measure the area.

	Estimate	Measure
	about ___ ▭	___ ▭
	about ___ ▭	___ ▭
	about ___ ▭	___ ▭
You choose.	about ___ ▭	___ ▭

Measurement 2-30

Comparing Units of Area

☐ Cover the shape with big 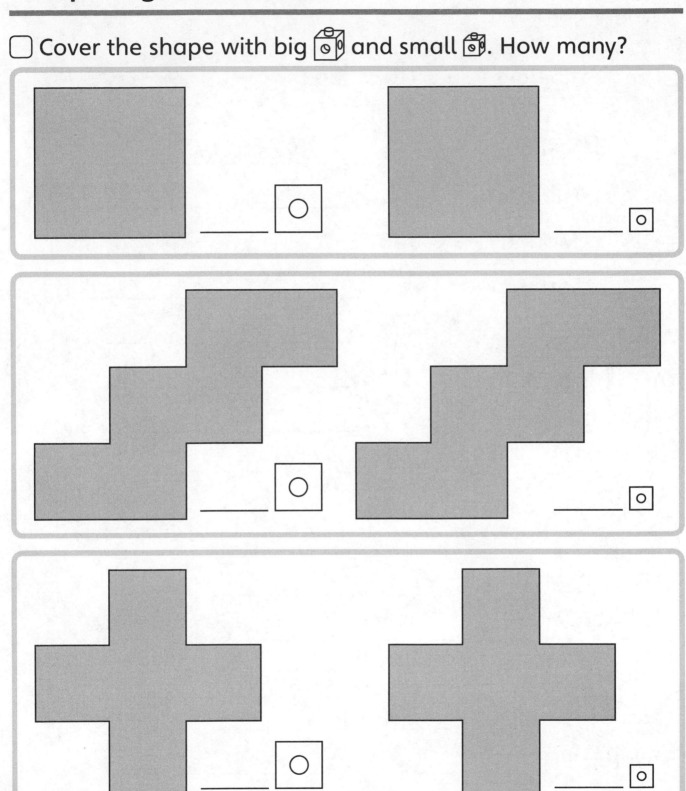 and small . How many?

☐ Did it take more big or more small
to cover the shapes? Why?

Days and Months

☐ Write the days of the week in order.
☐ Circle the days you go to school.

Friday	1. _____ *Sunday* _____
Thursday	2. _____
Monday	3. _____
Saturday	4. _____
Wednesday	5. _____
~~Sunday~~	6. _____
Tuesday	7. _____

☐ Unscramble the days.

ridFya	F r i d a y
noMyad	M ___ ___ d a y
Sduany	___ ___ ___ d a y
Tduaeys	___ ___ ___ ___ ___ ___ ___
rsudhaTy	___ ___ ___ ___ ___ ___ ___ ___
Syataurd	___ ___ ___ ___ ___ ___ ___ ___
aWdedsney	___ ___ ___ ___ ___ ___ ___ ___ ___

☐ Write the months of the year in order.
☐ Circle the months you go to school.

May	1. _____January_____
July	2. _____
December	3. _____
~~January~~	4. _____
March	5. _____
November	6. _____
September	7. _____
June	8. _____
February	9. _____
October	10. _____
August	11. _____
April	12. _____

☐ Unscramble the months.

yaM ___ ___ ___

eJun ___ ___ ___ ___

lyJu ___ ___ ___ ___

Bonus: ybrFeuar ___ ___ ___ ___ ___ ___ ___ ___

Calendars

☐ Use this calendar to answer the questions.

January 2018

Sunday	Monday	Tuesday	Wednesday	Thursday	Friday	Saturday
	1	2	3	4	5	6
7	8	9	10	11	12	13
14	15	16	17	18	19	20
21	22	23	24	25	26	27
28	29	30	31			

What day of the week is it?

January 1st _____ *Monday* _____

January 16th _____

January 25th _____

What date is each day?

the first Wednesday _____ *January 3rd* _____

the third Saturday _____

the second Monday _____

☐ Use this calendar to answer the questions.

June 2018						
Sunday	Monday	Tuesday	Wednesday	Thursday	Friday	Saturday
		Today ↓			1	2
3	4	5	6	7	8	9
10	11	12	13	14	15	16
17	18	19	20	21	22	23
24	25	26	27	28	29	30

Today is T ___ ___ ___ day, Ju ___ ___ 5th, ___ ___ 18

What **day** of the week was it yesterday? _____

What **date** will it be tomorrow? _____

Sara has a play date on June 15th.

How many **days** until her play date? _____

Is it more than 1 week, 1 week, or less than 1 week until

Sara's play date? _____

A class trip was exactly 1 month ago.

What **date** was the trip? _____

Thermometers

We use a **thermometer** to tell how **hot** or **cold** something is.

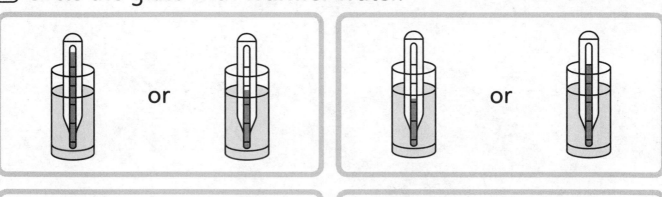

cold → warmer ↕ cooler hot

☐ Circle the glass with **warmer** water.

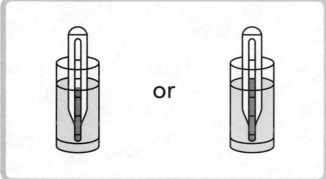

or

or

or

Bonus

or

As we heat water, it gets warmer.

☐ What happens 1st, 2nd, and 3rd? Write 1, 2, or 3.

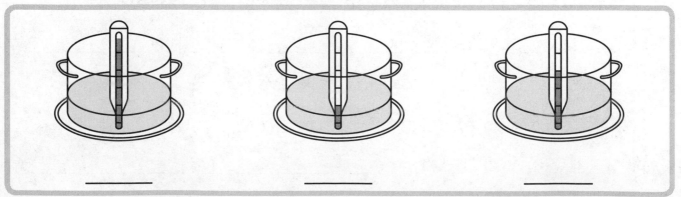

_____   _____   _____

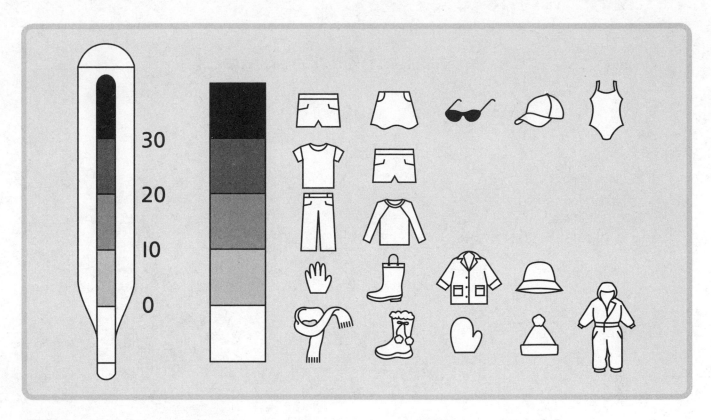

☐ Circle the clothes you need.

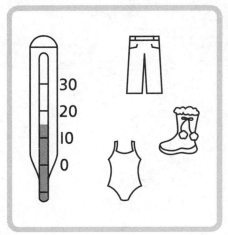

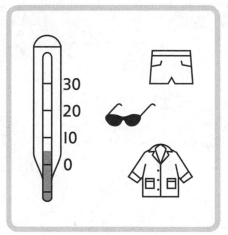

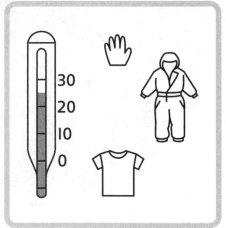

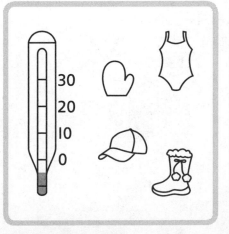

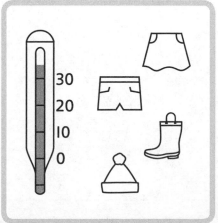

What Holds More?

☐ Write **less than**, **more than**, or **the same as**.

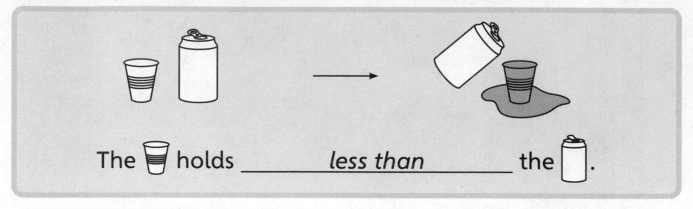

The 🥤 holds _____ *less than* _____ the 🥫.

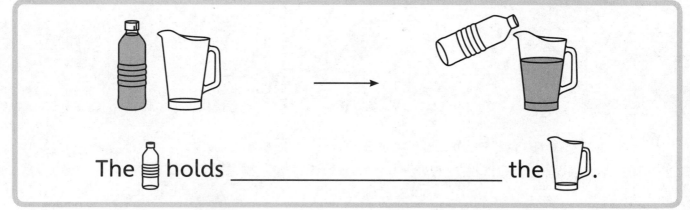

The 🍶 holds _____ the 🥛.

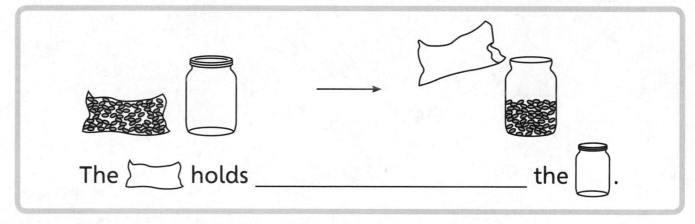

The ⬭ holds _____ the 🫙.

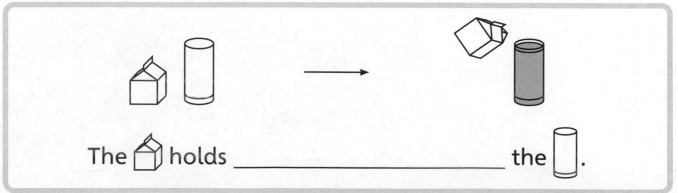

The 🧃 holds _____ the 🥛.

206

Capacity

☐ Write **less than**, **more than**, or **the same as**.

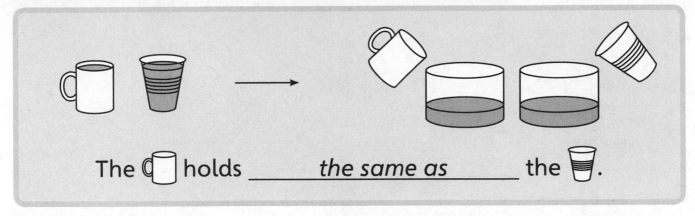

The 🍵 holds _____the same as_____ the 🥤.

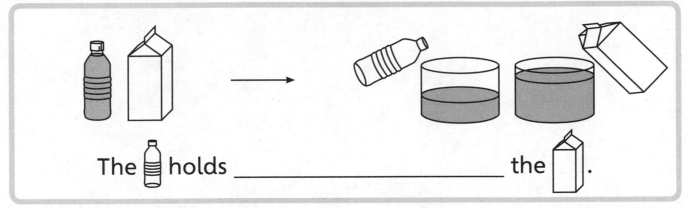

The 🍶 holds _____ the 🥛.

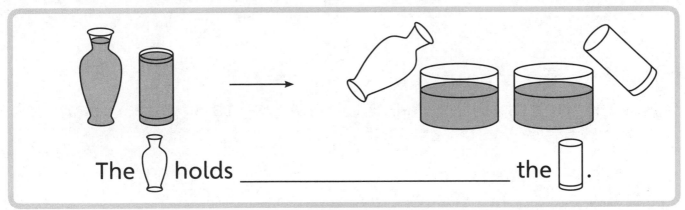

The 🏺 holds _____ the 🥫.

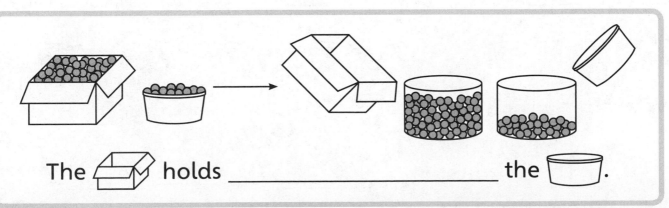

The 📦 holds _____ the 🥣.

Measuring Capacity

☐ Circle the container that holds **more**.

☐ What is the capacity of the containers?
☐ Order the containers from largest (1st) to smallest (3rd).

Measuring Cups

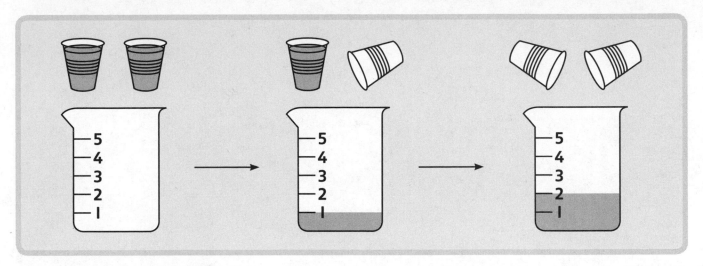

How much water?

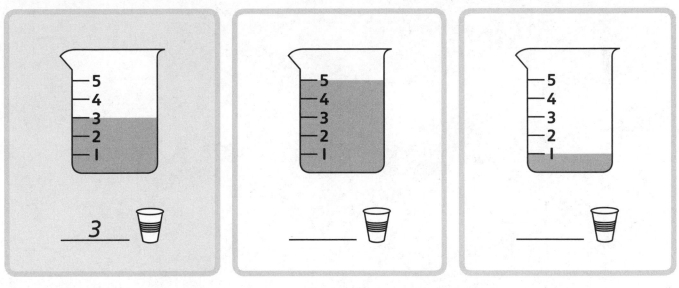

_____3_____

_____

_____

About how much water?

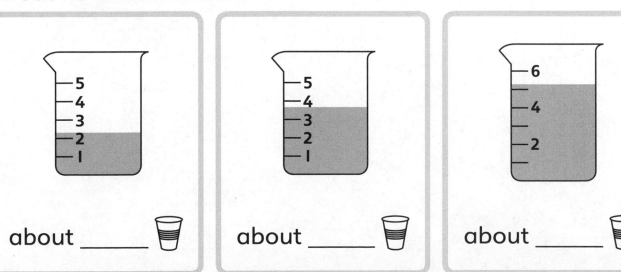

about _____

about _____

about _____